It's another great book from CGP...

OK, so GCSE Maths can be seriously challenging — and the latest exams are tougher than ever. The only way to master the skills you'll need is to practise answering questions until you're totally confident.

Luckily, this fantastic CGP Workbook is bursting with hundreds of practice questions covering every topic (with answers at the back) — all completely up-to-date for the new GCSE requirements.

You can thank us later. For now, we'd recommend getting stuck in...

CGP — still the best! ☺

Our sole aim here at CGP is to produce the highest quality books — carefully written, immaculately presented and dangerously close to being funny.

Then we work our socks off to get them out to you — at the cheapest possible prices.

Contents

Throughout the book, the more challenging questions are marked like this: **Q1**

Published by CGP

Illustrated by Ruso Bradley, Lex Ward and Ashley Tyson

From original material by Richard Parsons

Contributors:
Gill Allen,
JE Dodds,
Mark Haslam,
C McLoughlin,
John Waller,
Janet West,
Dave Williams.

Updated by: Joanna Daniels, Emily Garrett, Sarah Oxley, Andy Park, Caley Simpson, Ruth Wilbourne
With thanks to Shaun Harrogate, Simon Little and Alison Palin for the proofreading.

Printed by Elanders Ltd, Newcastle upon Tyne.
Clipart from Corel®

Text, design, layout and original illustrations © Richard Parsons 2015
All rights reserved.

Photocopying this book is not permitted. Extra copies are available from CGP with next day delivery.
0800 1712 712 • www.cgpbooks.co.uk

Types of Number and BODMAS

There are a few types of number that you really need to know — odd and even numbers, integers, prime numbers and rational and irrational numbers. Make sure you're happy with BODMAS too — that way you'll always do your calculations in the right order.

Q1 Sarah thinks of a positive number. She calculates that the square of the number is 256. What is the square root of the number?

Q2 Which of the following are integers?

$5 \qquad 6\frac{3}{4} \qquad 7.802 \qquad -87 \qquad -0.0003 \qquad 7.\dot{4} \qquad 167 \qquad \pi$

Q3 Which of these are rational and which are irrational?

a) $\sqrt[3]{25}$ **b)** $\sqrt{16}$ **c)** $\sqrt{5}$ **d)** $\frac{3}{8}$ **e)** $8.4\dot{2}$ **f)** 0.2413

Q4 1 is the first odd number. It is also the first square number and the first cube number. Which is greatest:
a) the third odd number, the third square number or the third cube number?
b) the sixth odd number, the fourth square number or the second cube number?

Q5 Using any or all of the figures **1, 2, 5, 9** write down:
a) the smallest prime number
b) a prime number greater than 20
c) a prime number between 10 and 20
d) two prime numbers whose sum is 21
e) a number that is not prime

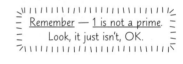

Remember — 1 is not a prime. Look, it just isn't, OK.

Q6 How many prime numbers are even?

Q7 What is the largest prime less than 120?

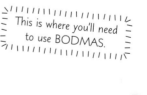

This is where you'll need to use BODMAS.

Q8 Without using a calculator, find the following:
a) $8 + 6 \times 2 - 5$
b) $(8 + 2) \div 5 + 2$
c) $(3 + 4) \times 8 - 3^3$
d) $6 \div 3 + 8 \times 2$
e) $(5 \times 2 - 2) \div 2$
f) $\sqrt{(12 - 3)} + 4 \times 2^2$
g) $\sqrt{8 + 17} + 3 \times 4$
h) $(4 \times 8 - 10 \times 3)^2$

Q9 Without using a calculator, find the reciprocal of $\sqrt{(2 + 3) \times 8 - 4}$.

Q10 Without using a calculator, decide which of the following has the largest value.

$6^2, \qquad 3^3, \qquad$ the prime number between 35 and 40, $\qquad 10 \times \sqrt{2 \times 5 + 6}$

Multiples, Factors and Prime Factors

Q1 From the numbers 1, 3, 6, 9 and 12, write down:

This is real basic stuff — you just have to know your times tables. And your primes, of course...

  a) a multiple of 4
  b) the prime number
  c) two square numbers
  d) three factors of 27
  e) two numbers, P and Q, that satisfy both $P = 2Q$ and $P = \sqrt{144}$

Q2 48 students went on a geography field trip. Their teachers split them into equal groups. Suggest five different ways that the teachers might have split up the students.

Q3 A school ran 3 evening classes: Conversational French, Cake Making and Woodturning. The Conversational French class had 29 students, Cake Making had 27 students, and the Woodturning class had 23. For which classes did the teacher have difficulty dividing the students into equal groups?

Q4 **a)** Write down the first five cube numbers.
  b) Which of the numbers given in part **a)** are multiples of 2?
  c) Which of the numbers given in part **a)** are multiples of 3?
  d) Which of the numbers given in part **a)** are multiples of 4?
  e) Which of the numbers given in part **a)** are multiples of 5?

Q5 Write down each number below as a product of its prime factors.

  a) 18
  b) 140
  c) 44
  d) 81

  e) 550
  f) 560
  g) 288
  h) 104

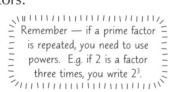
Remember — if a prime factor is repeated, you need to use powers. E.g. if 2 is a factor three times, you write 2^3.

Q6 Express the following numbers as products of their prime factors.

  a) 1050
  b) 1980
  c) 546

  d) 1260
  e) 462
  f) 3080

Q7 **a)** List the first five prime numbers.
  b) If added together, what is their total?
  c) Write down the answer to part **b)** as a product of its prime factors.

Multiples, Factors and Prime Factors

Q8 The prime factor decomposition of a certain number is $3^2 \times 5 \times 11$.
    a) Write down the number.
    b) Write down the prime factor decomposition of 165.

Q9 **a)** Write down the first ten square numbers.
    b) From your list, pick out all the multiples of 2.
    c) From your list, pick out all the multiples of 3.
    d) From your list, pick out any cube numbers.
    e) Add the numbers in your list together and write
        down the prime factor decomposition of the total.

Q10 Gordon is doing some woodwork and needs to calculate
the volume of a wooden rectangular block (a cuboid). The length
of the block is 50 cm, the height is 25 cm and the width is 16 cm.
    a) What is the volume (in cm³) of the wooden block?
    b) Express the number found in part **a)** as a product of its prime factors.
    c) Gordon needs to cut the block into smaller blocks with dimensions 4 cm × 5 cm × 5 cm.
        What is the maximum number of small blocks Gordon can make from the larger block?
        Make sure you show all your working.

Q11 The prime factor decomposition of a certain number is $2^3 \times 5 \times 17$.
    a) What is the number?
    b) What is the prime factor decomposition of half of this number?
    c) What is the prime factor decomposition of a quarter of the number?
    d) What is the prime factor decomposition of an eighth of the number?

Q12 Bryan and Sue were playing a guessing game. Sue thought of a number
between 1 and 100, which Bryan had to guess. Bryan was allowed to ask five
questions, which are listed with Sue's responses in the table below.

Bryan's Questions	Sue's Responses
Is it prime?	No
Is it odd?	No
Is it less than 50?	Yes
Is it a multiple of 3?	Yes
Is it a multiple of 7?	Yes

Use the questions
to narrow down the
possible numbers —
keep going until you
only have one left.

What is the number that Sue thought of?

LCM and HCF

Top tip LCM is the Least Common Multiple and HCF is the Highest Common Factor. The basic method is to list the multiples or factors of each number and pick out the answer. But sometimes the question will ask you to use prime factors to calculate the LCM or HCF — so make sure you can use this method too.

Q1 **a)** List the first ten multiples of 6, starting at 6.
b) List the first ten multiples of 5, starting at 5.
c) What is the LCM of 5 and 6?

Q2 **a)** List all the factors of 30.
b) List all the factors of 48.
c) What is the HCF of 30 and 48?

Q3 For each set of numbers find the HCF.
a) 40, 60
b) 10, 40, 60
c) 10, 24, 40, 60
d) 15, 45
e) 15, 30, 45
f) 15, 20, 30, 45
g) 32, 64
h) 32, 48, 64
i) 16, 32, 48, 64

Q4 For each set of numbers find the LCM.
a) 40, 60
b) 10, 40, 60
c) 10, 24, 40, 60
d) 15, 45
e) 15, 30, 45
f) 15, 20, 30, 45
g) 32, 64
h) 32, 48, 64
i) 16, 32, 48, 64

Q5 **a)** Express 15 and 18 as the product of their prime factors.
b) Using your answer to part **a)**, find the LCM of 15 and 18.

Q6 **a)** Express 90 and 120 as the product of their prime factors.
b) Using your answer to part **a)**, find the HCF of 90 and 120.

Q7 **a)** Given that $48 = 2^4 \times 3$ and $72 = 2^3 \times 3^2$, find the LCM of 48 and 72.
b) Given that $60 = 2^2 \times 3 \times 5$ and $126 = 2 \times 3^2 \times 7$, find the LCM of 60 and 126.

Q8 **a)** Given that $120 = 2^3 \times 3 \times 5$ and $150 = 2 \times 3 \times 5^2$, find the HCF of 120 and 150.
b) Given that $140 = 2^2 \times 5 \times 7$ and $600 = 2^3 \times 3 \times 5^2$, find the HCF of 140 and 600.

Q9 Lars, Rita and Alan regularly go swimming. Lars goes every 2 days, Rita goes every 3 days and Alan goes every 5 days. They all went swimming together on Friday 1st June.
a) On what date will Lars and Rita next go swimming together?
b) On what date will Rita and Alan next go swimming together?
c) On what day of the week will all three next go swimming together?
d) Which of the three (if any) will go swimming on 15th June?

This is just a LCM question in disguise.

Q10 Maggie has a lot of toy birds — 36 parrots, 42 puffins and 84 penguins. She wants to give them all away to some friends so that they each receive exactly the same number of toys, but they each get only one type of bird. What is the least number of friends she can give the toys away to?

Fractions

A page full of fractions, how exciting. I know you're itching to get started — just remember, you'll need to use common denominators when adding and subtracting.

Answer the following questions **without using a calculator.**

Q1 Carry out the following multiplications, giving your answers in their simplest form. Any answers larger than 1 should be given as an improper fraction.

Don't forget to see if you can cancel down before multiplying.

a) $\frac{1}{8} \times \frac{1}{8}$

c) $\frac{3}{18} \times \frac{1}{3}$

e) $\frac{6}{28} \times \frac{7}{15}$

b) $\frac{3}{32} \times \frac{4}{11}$

d) $1\frac{1}{4} \times 3\frac{1}{8}$

f) $\frac{9}{10} \times \frac{9}{100} \times \frac{1}{100}$

Q2 Carry out the following divisions, giving your answers in their lowest terms.

'Lowest terms' and 'simplest form' mean the same thing — just cancel down as far as you can.

a) $\frac{1}{8} \div \frac{1}{8}$

c) $\frac{3}{18} \div \frac{1}{3}$

e) $1\frac{1}{4} \div 4\frac{1}{8}$

b) $\frac{2}{3} \div \frac{1}{6}$

d) $1\frac{1}{4} \div 3\frac{1}{8}$

f) $\left(\frac{9}{10} \div \frac{9}{100}\right) \div \frac{1}{100}$

Q3 Evaluate the following, giving your answers in their simplest form. Give any answers that are larger than 1 as improper fractions.

a) $\frac{1}{8} + \frac{1}{8}$

c) $\frac{3}{4} + \frac{7}{15}$

e) $1\frac{3}{4} + 4\frac{4}{5}$

b) $\frac{1}{6} + \frac{2}{3}$

d) $1\frac{1}{4} + 3\frac{1}{8}$

f) $\frac{9}{10} + \frac{9}{20} + \frac{1}{30}$

Q4 Caley is making some punch for her birthday party. She mixes $\frac{1}{2}$ litre of cranberry juice, $1\frac{1}{2}$ litres of apple juice, $\frac{2}{3}$ litre of orange juice and $\frac{4}{5}$ litre of pineapple juice. She has a bowl that will hold $3\frac{1}{2}$ litres. Is this big enough to contain all of the punch?

Q5 Evaluate the following, giving your answers in their simplest form. Give any answers that are larger than 1 as improper fractions.

a) $\frac{7}{8} - \frac{2}{8}$

c) $\frac{3}{4} - \frac{1}{3}$

e) $1\frac{1}{8} - 4\frac{3}{5}$

b) $\frac{2}{3} - \frac{1}{6}$

d) $3\frac{1}{8} - 1\frac{1}{4}$

f) $\left(\frac{9}{10} - \frac{9}{100}\right) - \frac{1}{30}$

Q6 Evaluate the following, giving your answers in their lowest terms. Give any answers that are larger than 1 as mixed numbers.

a) $\frac{1}{2} + \frac{1}{4}$

e) $6 \times \frac{2}{3}$

i) $3 + \frac{8}{5}$

b) $\frac{2}{3} - \frac{1}{4}$

f) $\frac{4}{5} \div \frac{2}{3}$

j) $\frac{2}{3}\left(\frac{3}{4} + \frac{4}{5}\right)$

c) $\frac{1}{5} + \frac{2}{3} - \frac{2}{5}$

g) $\frac{5}{12} \times \frac{3}{2}$

k) $\left(\frac{1}{7} + \frac{3}{14}\right) \times \left(3 - \frac{1}{5}\right)$

d) $5 - \frac{1}{4}$

h) $\frac{5}{6} - \frac{7}{8}$

l) $\left(\frac{3}{4} - \frac{1}{5}\right) \div \left(\frac{7}{8} + \frac{1}{16}\right)$

Fractions

The cunning bit with long wordy questions is picking out the important bits and then translating them into numbers. It's not that easy at first, but you'll get better.

Answer questions 7 – 9 **without using your calculator**.

Q7 Write each of these times as a fraction of 1 hour. Give each fraction in its simplest form.
   a) 5 minutes   **b)** 15 minutes   **c)** 40 minutes

Q8 The Sandwich Club of Great Britain are going on their annual picnic.
   a) The boxes they use to transport their sandwiches are 10 inches high with a base the same size as a single sandwich. Each sandwich is $\frac{5}{8}$ inch thick. How many boxes will they need for 80 sandwiches?
   b) How tall would the box need to be if 40 sandwiches were to be stacked inside?

Q9 Steve owns 160 farm animals. $\frac{5}{32}$ of them are sheep and $\frac{2}{5}$ of the sheep are lambs. How many lambs does Steve own?

You can **use your calculator** for questions 10 – 13.

Q10 The amount of sugar in Healthybix cereal has been reduced by $\frac{1}{4}$. There is now 4.8 g of sugar in every 50 g of cereal. Work out the original amount of sugar in 50 g of the cereal.

Q11 Louise, Sophie and Rebekah each buy the same dress at different discounted prices. They get $\frac{7}{15}$, $\frac{4}{9}$ and $\frac{13}{27}$ off the original price, respectively. The dress originally cost £49.95.
   a) Who gets the biggest discount?
   b) Charlotte later buys the dress from Sophie, but gets a further $\frac{1}{5}$ off the price Sophie paid. How much does the dress cost Charlotte?

Q12 George wants to make a cake. The recipe requires 150 g each of flour, sugar and butter, and 3 eggs. George only has 2 eggs so he decides to make a smaller cake with the same proportions.
   a) How much flour will George need to use?
   b) If each egg weighs 25 g, how much will the cake weigh before it goes in the oven?
   c) What fraction of the uncooked weight is flour? Simplify your answer.
   d) If the cake loses $\frac{1}{7}$ of its weight during baking (due to moisture loss), what will it weigh after baking?

Q13 The diagram shows 3 identical trapeziums, each with a different area shaded. Trapezium A has $\frac{1}{9}$ of its area shaded and trapezium B has $\frac{3}{8}$ of its area shaded. What fraction of trapezium C is shaded?

Fractions, Decimals and Percentages

I reckon that converting decimals to percentages is about as easy as it gets — so make the most of it.

Answer questions 1 – 4 **without using your calculator**.

Q1 Express each of the following as a percentage.

a) 0.25   c) 0.75   e) 0.4152   g) 0.06
b) 0.5   d) 0.1   f) 0.8406   h) 0.2828

Q2 Express each percentage as a decimal.

a) 50%   c) 40%   e) 60.2%   g) 43.1%
b) 12%   d) 34%   f) 8%   h) 6.8%

Q3 Express each of the following as a percentage.

a) $\frac{1}{2}$ c) $\frac{3}{4}$ e) $\frac{2}{5}$ g) $\frac{11}{20}$

b) $\frac{1}{8}$ d) $\frac{5}{4}$ f) $\frac{1}{25}$ h) $\frac{9}{200}$

For f) and g), start by finding an equivalent fraction with denominator 100...

Q4 Express each percentage as a fraction in its simplest form.

a) 25%   e) 7.5%
b) 60%   f) 49.6%
c) 45%   g) 88.6%
d) 30%   h) 32.4%

Best thing to do with e)-h) is to put them over 100, then get rid of the <u>decimal point</u> by <u>multiplying</u> top and bottom by 10. Then just <u>cancel down</u> as normal.

You can **use your calculator** for questions 5 – 7.

Q5 Express each of the following as a percentage. Give your answers to 2 decimal places.

a) $\frac{6}{13}$ c) $\frac{4}{15}$ e) $\frac{3}{11}$

b) $\frac{1}{6}$ d) $\frac{9}{7}$ f) $\frac{11}{3}$

Q6 119 out of 140 houses on an estate have DVD players. What percentage is this?

Q7 In an exam Tina scored 52/80. The grade she receives depends on the percentage scored. What grade will Tina get?

Grades	
51-60%	5
61-70%	6
71-80%	7
81-90%	8
91-100%	9

Fractions, Decimals and Percentages

This page gets a bit tricky towards the end. Make sure you know the methods for converting between recurring decimals and fractions — then you won't get in a tizz.

Answer these questions **without using a calculator**.

Q8 Write the following fractions as decimals.

a) $\frac{3}{10}$ b) $\frac{37}{100}$ c) $\frac{2}{5}$ d) $\frac{3}{8}$

e) $\frac{14}{8}$ f) $\frac{17}{25}$ g) $\frac{24}{40}$ h) $\frac{4}{80}$

You should cancel down fractions as far as possible before converting to a decimal.

Q9 Fill in the gaps in the following conversion table.

Decimal	0.5		0.125	1.6				0.45
Fraction	$\frac{1}{2}$	$\frac{1}{5}$			$\frac{1}{4}$	$\frac{7}{2}$	$\frac{3}{20}$	

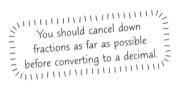

Q10 Write the following fractions as recurring decimals.

a) $\frac{5}{6}$ b) $\frac{7}{9}$ c) $\frac{7}{11}$ d) $\frac{47}{99}$

e) $\frac{10}{11}$ f) $\frac{29}{33}$ g) $\frac{478}{999}$ h) $\frac{5891}{9999}$

Q11 Write the following decimals as fractions in their simplest form.

a) 0.6   b) 0.75   c) 0.95   d) 0.128

e) $0.\dot{3}$ f) $0.\dot{6}$ g) $0.\dot{1}$ h) $0.\dot{1}\dot{6}$

Q12 Write the following recurring decimals as fractions in their lowest terms.

a) 0.222...   b) 0.444...   c) 0.888...   d) 0.808080...

e) 0.121212...   f) 0.545545545...   g) 0.753753753   h) 0.156156156...

Q13 Convert the following recurring decimals to fractions in their simplest form.

a) $0.1\dot{3}$ b) $0.7\dot{8}$ c) $0.0\dot{8}$ d) $0.13\dot{4}$

e) $0.8\dot{6}\dot{4}$ f) $0.00\dot{6}\dot{0}$ g) $0.21\dot{3}$ h) $0.6\dot{4}0\dot{3}$

Rounding Numbers

 With all these rounding methods, you need to identify the last digit — e.g. if you're rounding **23.41** to 1 decimal place the last digit is **4**. Then look at the next digit to the right. If it's **5** or more you round up, if it's **4** or less you leave the last digit as it is.

Q1 Round these numbers to the required number of decimal places.

 a) 62.1935 (1 d.p.)   **d)** 19.624328 (5 d.p.)   **g)** 739.995 (2 d.p.)
 b) 62.1935 (2 d.p.)   **e)** 6.2999 (3 d.p.)   **h)** 54.0505 (3 d.p.)
 c) 62.1935 (3 d.p.)   **f)** π (3 d.p.)   **i)** 5.8̇ (3 d.p.)

Q2 Round these numbers to the required number of significant figures.

 a) 1329.62 (3 s.f.)   **d)** 120 (1 s.f.)
 b) 1329.62 (4 s.f.)   **e)** 0.024087 (1 s.f.)
 c) 1329.62 (5 s.f.)   **f)** 0.024087 (4 s.f.)

Remember — the first significant figure is the first digit which isn't zero.

Q3 $K = 456.9873$
Write *K* correct to:

 a) one decimal place   **d)** three significant figures
 b) two decimal places   **e)** two significant figures
 c) three decimal places   **f)** one significant figure

Q4 Round these prices to the nearest pound.

 a) £1100.45   **d)** £2.55
 b) £87.61   **e)** £376.49
 c) £299.50   **f)** £44.19

Q5 A bumper bag of icing sugar weighs 23.4 kg.
What is this correct to the nearest kilogram?

Q6 Pru measured the length of her bedroom as 2.345 metres. Round this measurement correct to the nearest centimetre. Give your answer in metres.

Q7 Jessy jumps 4.65 m in the long jump. What is this to the nearest ten centimetres? Give your answer in metres.

Q8 Jack's company pays his travel expenses.
They round the distance he drives to the nearest mile, and then pay 20p for every mile.
In one week, Jack drives 95.45 miles. How much money can Jack claim back?

Q9 A pack of three model cars costs £14.30. John wants to work out the cost per car.
What is the answer correct to the nearest penny?

Q10 A baby sea turtle weighs 1815.56 g.
How much does it weigh to 3 significant figures?

Estimating

Get your thinking cap on — you'll need to do this page <u>without a calculator.</u>

Q1   Mark wants to buy some tropical fish.
The pet shop owner tells him that he will need
a tank with a volume of at least 7000 cm³.
Estimate whether Mark's tank will be big enough.

10.4 cm

14.8 cm

29.6 cm

Q2   Find approximate answers to the following:

a) 6560 × 1.97

b) 38.45 × 1.4237 × 5.0002

c) 45.34 ÷ 9.345

d) 34504 ÷ 7133

e) $\dfrac{55.33 \times 19.345}{9.23}$

f) $\dfrac{149.5 + 49.1}{153.2 - 48.2}$

g) $\dfrac{821.43 - 219.86}{0.98 + 8.91}$

h) $\dfrac{78.9 \times 304.8}{58.39 \div 21.66}$

i) $\dfrac{1318.46 \div 2.164}{5.138 \times 11.421}$

j) π ÷ 3

Round these to nice easy numbers that you can deal with without a calculator.

Q3   At the start of the week, a shop had approximately 15 000 cartons of broccoli juice in
stock. The shop sold 1483 cartons on Monday, 2549 on Tuesday, 1539 on Wednesday,
1478 on Thursday and 2958 on Friday. Estimate the number of cartons remaining.

Q4   Showing all your working, estimate the value of the following:

a) $\dfrac{18.2 \times 10.7}{\sqrt{398.6}}$

b) $\dfrac{(9.7)^2 \div 10.3}{4.306 \times 5.011}$

c) $\dfrac{6.42 \times 8.803}{0.321}$

d) $\dfrac{\sqrt{98.6}}{0.3301 + 0.192}$

Q5   Joan needs to estimate the size of her bedroom so that she can buy enough paint to
cover the walls. Two of the walls measure 2.86 m by 3.16 m, and the other two
walls measure 2.86 m by 3.42 m.
a) Estimate the area that Joan needs to paint in m².
b) If one tin of paint will cover 15 m², how many tins of paint will Joan need to paint
her bedroom?

Q6   For each diagram below, estimate the volume shown. Explain whether
your estimate will be larger or smaller than the actual volume.

a)

←10 cm→

19.8 cm

b)

← 4 cm →

9.7 cm

3.1 cm

For this, you'll need the
formula for the volume
of a cylinder: V = πr²h

Q7   Estimate the following roots, to 1 decimal place.

a) $\sqrt{48}$

b) $\sqrt{118}$

c) $\sqrt{84}$

d) $\sqrt{17}$

e) $\sqrt[3]{10}$

f) $\sqrt[3]{25}$

Start with roots that you know — and use them to make an educated guess.

Bounds

Bounds are useful when you're dealing with rounded numbers — they tell you the range of values that the original unrounded number lies in. Remember, when a number's been rounded to a given unit, the actual value can be up to half a unit bigger or smaller.

Q1   Jodie weighs herself on some scales that are accurate to the nearest 10 grams.
       The digital display shows her weight as 64.78 kg.
   a) What is the maximum that she could weigh?
   b) What is the minimum that she could weigh?

Q2   A rectangular rug is 1.8 metres long and 0.7 metres wide.
       Both measurements are given correct to one decimal place.

   a) State the minimum possible length of the rug.
   b) Calculate the maximum possible area of the rug.

> Truncating is different from rounding — the number is just cut off.

Q3 a) The height, h, of the Eiffel Tower is 300.6 m truncated to
       1 decimal place. Express the possible values of the height as an inequality.
   b) The width of the base of the Eiffel Tower, when truncated to a whole
       number, is 125 m. What is the minimum possible width of the base?

Q4   It's Pancake Day and Nigel is making a large batch of pancakes to share with friends.
       His recipe tells him to add 2.5 litres of milk, but his measuring jug only measures up
       to 500 ml and is accurate to the nearest 10 ml.
   a) What is the maximum volume of milk Nigel could measure out,
       assuming he is as accurate as he can be?
   b) What is the minimum volume of milk Nigel could measure out?

Q5   Sandra has a parcel to post. She weighs it to find out the cost of postage.
   a) A set of kitchen scales, that weigh to the nearest 10 g, show that the weight of the
       parcel is 90 g. Find the interval in which the actual weight, p, of the parcel lies.
   b) Next she weighs the parcel on a different set of kitchen scales,
       which are accurate to the nearest 5 g. The parcel weighs 95 g.
       Give the interval in which p lies according to these scales.
   c) The post office weighs the parcel on some electronic scales to the nearest gram.
       It weighs 98 g. Can all the scales be right? Explain your answer.

Q6   A village hall contains 125 chairs to the nearest 5.
   a) What are the upper and lower bounds for the number of chairs?
   b) A meeting is going to take place in the village hall. The number of people
       expected to attend is 130 to the nearest 5. Is it possible that everyone expected
       will be able to sit down at the meeting? Explain your reasoning.

Bounds

Q7 Jimmy, Sarah and Douglas are comparing their best times for running the 1500 m. Jimmy's best time is 5 minutes 30 seconds measured to the nearest 10 seconds. Sarah's best time is also 5 minutes 30 seconds, but measured to the nearest 5 seconds. Douglas' best time is 5 minutes 26 seconds measured to the nearest second.

    a) What are the upper and lower bounds for Sarah's best time?

    b) Douglas thinks that he is the quickest at running the 1500 m. Explain why this may not be the case.

To find the upper or lower bound of a <u>calculation</u>, you've just got to decide which version of the values involved (max or min) to use to get the biggest or smallest overall answer. And remember — you don't always get the maximum value by using the biggest input values.

Q8 $A = 13$, correct to 2 significant figures.
    $B = 12.5$, correct to 3 significant figures.

    a) For the value of A, write down the upper bound and the lower bound.

    b) For the value of B, write down the upper bound and the lower bound.

    c) Calculate the upper bound and lower bound for C when $C = AB$. Using these values, express the interval in which C lies as an inequality.

Q9 Ash wants to put a new carpet in his living room. He has measured the floor as being 3.4 m × 5.2 m to the nearest 10 cm. There is a discount available at the local carpet shop for anyone who buys more than 18.5 m² of carpet. If Ash buys enough carpet to be sure he can cover the whole floor, will he receive the discount? Explain your answer.

Q10 a) The length of a rectangle is measured as 12 ± 0.1 cm. The width of the same rectangle is measured as 4 ± 0.1 cm. Calculate the perimeter of the rectangle, giving also the maximum possible error.

You need to add the errors for all the sides together.

    b) A rectangle measures $A ± x$ cm in length and $B ± y$ cm in width. The formula $P = 2(A + B)$ is used to calculate the perimeter, P, of the rectangle. What is the maximum possible error in P?

Q11 A lorry travelled 125 kilometres in 1 hour and 50 minutes. If the time was measured to the nearest 10 minutes and the distance to the nearest 5 kilometres, what is the maximum value of the average speed of the lorry, in kilometres per hour?

Q12 $R = \dfrac{S}{T}$ is a formula used by stockbrokers.

    $S = 940$, correct to 2 significant figures and $T = 5.56$, correct to 3 significant figures.

    a) For the value of S, write down the upper bound and the lower bound.

    b) For the value of T, write down the upper bound and the lower bound.

    c) Calculate the upper bound and the lower bound for R.

    d) Write down the value of R correct to an appropriate number of significant figures.

Standard Form

Writing very big (or very small) numbers gets a bit messy if you don't use standard form — because of all those zeros. But of course, the main reason for knowing about standard form is... you guessed it — it's in the Exam.

Q1 Delilah is doing some calculations for her science homework.
She needs to give her answers as ordinary numbers.
How should she write the following answers?

a) 3.56×10
b) 3.56×10^3
c) 3.56×10^{-1}
d) 3.56×10^4

e) 0.082×10^2
f) 0.082×10^{-2}
g) 0.082×10
h) 0.082×10^{-1}

i) 157×10
j) 157×10^{-3}
k) 157×10^3
l) 157×10^{-1}

Q2 Write in standard form:

a) 2.56
b) 25.6
c) 0.256
d) 25 600

e) 95.2
f) 0.0952
g) 95 200
h) 0.000952

i) 4200
j) 0.0042
k) 42
l) 420

Q3 Write in standard form:

a) 34.7×10
b) 73.004
c) 0.005×10^3
d) 9183×10^2

e) 15 million
f) 937.1×10^4
g) 0.000075
h) 0.05×10^{-2}

i) 534×10^{-2}
j) 621.03
k) 149×10^2
l) 0.003×10^{-4}

Q4 A tissue sample is three cells thick. Each cell has a thickness of 0.000004 m.
What is the thickness of the tissue sample in mm? Give your answer in standard form.

Q5 This table gives the diameter and distance from the Sun of some planets.

Planet	Distance from Sun (km)	Diameter (km)
Earth	1.5×10^8	1.3×10^4
Venus	1.085×10^8	1.2×10^4
Mars	2.28×10^8	6.8×10^3
Mercury	5.81×10^7	4.9×10^3
Jupiter	7.8×10^8	1.4×10^5
Neptune	4.52×10^9	4.9×10^4
Saturn	1.43×10^9	1.2×10^5

From the table write down which planet is:
a) smallest in diameter
b) largest in diameter
c) nearest to the Sun
d) furthest from the Sun

Write down which planets are:
e) nearer to the Sun than the Earth is
f) bigger in diameter than the Earth

Q6 The following numbers are <u>not</u> written in standard form.
Rewrite them correctly using standard form.

a) 42×10^6
b) 38×10^{-5}
c) 10×10^6

d) 11.2×10^{-5}
e) 843×10^3
f) 42.32×10^{-4}

g) 17×10^{17}
h) 28.3×10^{-5}
i) 10×10^{-3}

Standard Form

I know you enjoyed that last page on standard form, so here's another. I'm so kind...

Answer questions 7, 9 and 13 to 16 **without using a calculator**.

Q7 Work out the answers to these calculations. Write your answers in standard form.
- **a)** $(3 \times 10^4) \times (6.3 \times 10^2)$
- **b)** $(2.8 \times 10^5) \div (1.4 \times 10^3)$
- **c)** $800\,000 \times (9.2 \times 10^7)$
- **d)** $(8.9 \times 10^3) + (3.1 \times 10^4)$
- **e)** $50\,000 + (3.6 \times 10^5)$
- **f)** $(1.8 \times 10^4) - (5.2 \times 10^3)$

Q8 Evaluate the following, writing your answers in standard form.
- **a)** $(2.85 \times 10^3) \times (3.2 \times 10^6)$
- **b)** $(4.93 \times 10^6) \div (8.5 \times 10^4)$
- **c)** $(9.63 \times 10^5) + (2.4 \times 10^6)$
- **d)** $(4.35 \times 10^6) - (2.7 \times 10^3)$

Q9 If $x = 4 \times 10^5$ and $y = 6 \times 10^4$ work out the value of the following. Give your answers in standard form.
- **a)** xy
- **b)** $4x$
- **c)** $3y$

Q10 Which is greater, 4.62×10^{12} or 1.04×10^{13}, and by how much?

Q11 Which is smaller, 3.2×10^{-8} or 1.3×10^{-9}, and by how much?

Q12 a) The surface area of the Earth is 5.1×10^8 km². Write this <u>without</u> using standard form.
b) The area of the Earth covered by sea is $362\,000\,000$ km². Write this in standard form.
c) What is the area of the Earth covered by land? Write your answer <u>without</u> using standard form.

Q13 Write the following in standard form.
- **a)** $2^{15} \times 5^{17}$
- **b)** $2^{-20} \times 5^{-21}$
- **c)** $\dfrac{1}{2 \times 5^{-2}}$

Use the power rules to rearrange these into the form $a \times 10^b$.

Q14 Find values of x, y and z that satisfy the following calculation:
$(8 \times 10^x) + (6 \times 10^y) + (2 \times 10^z) = 80\,620$

Q15 Work out the answers to these calculations. Write your answers in standard form.

- **a)** $\dfrac{(6.3 \times 10^8) \times (2 \times 10^4)}{(2 \times 10^6) \times (1.5 \times 10^3)}$
- **b)** $\dfrac{(8.5 \times 10^{12}) \times (3 \times 10^{14})}{(1.6 \times 10^{10}) \div (3.2 \times 10^9)}$
- **c)** $\dfrac{(3 \times 10^{12}) \times (6 \times 10^{-8})}{(2 \times 10^{-2}) \times (3 \times 10^3)}$
- **d)** $\dfrac{(3.12 \times 10^{-6}) \div (2 \times 10^{-10})}{(2.95 \times 10^{27}) + (5 \times 10^{25})}$

Q16 There are 6.02×10^{23} carbon atoms in 12 g of carbon.
- **a)** Estimate the mass of one atom of carbon.
- **b)** State whether the actual mass of one carbon atom is greater or smaller than your answer to a).

Algebra Basics

Make sure you've got to grips with these questions before you get on with the rest of the section — they'll give you a bit of practice at the basic algebra skills you'll need...

Q1 Work out the following temperature changes.
a) 20 °C to -7 °C
b) -10 °C to -32 °C
c) -17 °C to -5 °C
d) -3 °C to 15 °C
e) -31 °C to -16 °C
f) -5 °C to -17 °C

Q2 Which is larger and by how much?
a) -12 + 7 – -4 + 6 – 2 + 7 or **b)** -30 + 26 – 3 – -7 + 17

Q3 Simplify: **a)** $4x - -5x + 3x - x + 2x - 7x$ **b)** $30y - 10y + 2y - 3y + 4y - -5y$

Q4 Find the value of xy and $\frac{x}{y}$ for each of the following:
a) $x = -100$ $y = 10$
b) $x = 24$ $y = -4$
c) $x = -48$ $y = -3$
d) $x = 0$ $y = -4$

Q5 Find the value of $(a - b) \div (c + d)$ when $a = 10$, $b = -26$, $c = -5$ and $d = -4$.

Q6 Simplify the following:
a) $2x \times -3y$
b) $-8a \times 2b$
c) $-4x \times -2x$
d) $4p \times -4p$
e) $-30x \div -3y$
f) $50x \div -5y$
g) $10x \div -2y$
h) $-30x \div -10x$
i) $40ab \div -10ab$
j) $70x^2 \div -7x^2$
k) $-36x^2 \div -9x$
l) $40y^2 \div -5y$

Q7 Simplify the following by collecting like terms together.
a) $3x^2 + 4x + 12x^2 - 5x$
b) $14x^2 - 10x - x^2 + 5x$
c) $12 - 4x^2 + 10x - 3x^2 + 2x$
d) $20abc + 12ab + 10bac + 4b$
e) $8pq + 7p + q + 10qp - q + p$
f) $15ab - 10a + b - 7a + 2ba$
g) $4pq - 14p - 8q + p - q + 8p$
h) $13x^2 + 4x^2 - 5y^2 + y^2 - x^2$
i) $11ab + 2cd - ba - 13dc + abc$
j) $3x^2 + 4xy + 2y^2 - z^2 + 2xy - y^2 - 5x^2$

Q8 For each of the diagrams below, write down the area of each of the small rectangles and hence find an expression for the area of each large rectangle.

a)

b)

c)

Eeeek — loads of questions...

Powers and Roots

Hang on there. Before you try this page, make sure you know all the rules for dealing with powers.

Remember, 2^4 means 'two to the power four'.

Q1 Complete the following:
a) $2^4 = 2 \times 2 \times 2 \times 2 \quad =$
b) $10^3 = 10 \times 10 \times 10 =$
c) $3^5 = 3 \times ... \qquad =$
d) $1^9 = 1 \times ... \qquad =$

Q2 Simplify the following:
a) $2 \times 2 \times 2 \times 2 \times 2 \times 2 \times 2 \times 2$
b) $12 \times 12 \times 12 \times 12 \times 12$
c) $m \times m \times m$
d) $z \times z \times z \times z \times z \times z$

Q3 Complete the following (the first one has been done for you):
a) $10^2 \times 10^3 = (10 \times 10) \times (10 \times 10 \times 10) = 10^5$
b) $10^3 \times 10^4 = \qquad =$
c) $10^5 \times 10^3 = \qquad =$
d) What is the <u>quick method</u> for writing down the final result in **b)** and **c)**?

Easy — you'll have learnt this from your power rules.

Q4 Complete the following (the first one has been done for you):
a) $2^4 \div 2^2 = \dfrac{(2 \times 2 \times 2 \times 2)}{(2 \times 2)} = 2^2$
c) $4^5 \div 4^3 = \dfrac{(4 \times 4 \times 4 \times 4 \times 4)}{} =$
b) $2^5 \div 2^2 = \qquad =$
d) $8^5 \div 8^2 = \qquad =$
e) What is the <u>quick method</u> for writing down the final result in **b)**, **c)** and **d)**?

Q5 **Without using a calculator**, decide which of the following are <u>true</u>.
a) $2^4 \times 2^6 = 2^{10}$
b) $2^2 \times 2^3 \times 2^4 = 2^9$
c) $2^3 \times 2^2 = 2^6$
d) $4^{10} \times 4^4 \times (4^2)^3 = 4^{18}$
e) $2^1 \times (2^3)^4 \times 2^4 = 2^{17}$
f) $10^4 \times (10^2)^3 = 10^8$
g) $2^{20} \div 2^5 = 2^4$
h) $3^{12} \div 3^4 = 3^8$
i) $4^6 \div 6^4 = 4^2$
j) $10^{20} \div (10^3)^2 = 10^{14}$
k) $4^6 \div (4^2 \times 4^3) = 4^1$
l) $9^2 \times (9^{30} \div 9^{25}) = 9^{10}$

Q6 For each of the following, answer **true** or **false**:
a) When x is a negative number, x^2 is always positive.
b) When x is a positive whole number, x^4 is always greater than x.
c) For all values of x, a and b, $x^a \times x^b = x^{a \times b}$.

Q7 Remove the brackets from the following and express as a single power.
a) $(3^4 \times 3^2) \div (3^6 \times 3^3)$
b) $(4^{10} \times 4^{12}) \times 4^3$
c) $10^2 \div (10^3 \times 10^{12})$
d) $(3^6)^{-2}$
e) $4^2 \times 4^{-1} \times 4^6 \times (4^2 \div 4^3)$
f) $(5^2 \times 5^3) \div (5^6 \div 5^4)$
g) $(2^7 \times 2^{-1}) \times (2^2 \div 2^5)$
h) $(10^3 \div 10^{-5}) \times (10^4 \div 10^2)$
i) $(7^4 \div 7^{-3}) \div (7^{-8} \times 7^{-5})$
j) $(3^{\frac{1}{5}} \times 3^{\frac{3}{5}}) \div 3^{\frac{2}{5}}$
k) $(4^{-\frac{3}{4}} \times 4^{\frac{1}{4}}) \div 4^{-\frac{1}{4}}$
l) $(2^{\frac{2}{3}} \times 2^{-\frac{1}{3}}) \div (2^{-\frac{5}{3}} \times 2^{\frac{1}{3}})$

Q8 Simplify the following:
a) $x^2 \times x^3$
b) $y^5 \div y^4$
c) $(a^4)^3$
d) $f^1 \times f^4$
e) z^0
f) $\left(\dfrac{2x}{y}\right)^3 \times x^4$
g) $5b^{-3} \times 6b^{-2}$
h) $(3x^3y^4)^2$
i) $3a^3b^2 \times 2a^5b^3$
j) $4p^{-10}q^4 \times 2p^8q^{-15}$
k) $8x^5y^7 \div 4x^3y^4$
l) $121c^2d^3 \div 11c^7d^9$
m) $7a^5b^{-3} \times 4a^{-2}b^4$
n) $(16x^4)^{\frac{1}{2}} \times (27x^6)^{\frac{1}{3}}$
o) $(4x^2)^{\frac{3}{2}} \div (2x^{\frac{1}{3}})^3$
p) $(9y^{-\frac{2}{5}})^{\frac{3}{2}} \div (3y^{-\frac{1}{5}})^2$

Powers and Roots

Use your **calculator** to evaluate the expressions in questions 9 to 13.
Give your answers as decimals to 3 s.f. where necessary.

Q9
a) $(6.5)^3$
b) $(0.35)^2$
c) $(15.2)^4$
d) $(0.04)^3$

e) $\sqrt{5.6}$
f) $\sqrt[3]{12.4}$
g) $\sqrt{109}$
h) $\sqrt[3]{0.6}$

i) $(1\frac{1}{2})^2$
j) $\sqrt{4\frac{3}{4}}$
k) $\left(\frac{5}{8}\right)^3$
l) $\sqrt[3]{\frac{9}{10}}$

Q10
a) $(2.4)^2 + 3$
b) $5.9 - (1.2)^3$
c) $\sqrt[3]{5.6} + (4.2)^2$

d) $(6.05)^3 - \sqrt[3]{8.4}$
e) $6.1[35.4 - (4.2)^2]$
f) $95 - 3(\sqrt[3]{48} - 2.6)$

g) $1\frac{1}{2}[4 + (2\frac{1}{4})^2]$
h) $19 - 4\left[\left(\frac{1}{4}\right)^2 + \left(\frac{5}{8}\right)^3\right]$
i) $15\frac{3}{5} - 2\frac{1}{2}\left[\left(1\frac{3}{4}\right)^3 - \sqrt[3]{1\frac{1}{2}}\right]$

Q11
a) 1.7^{-3}
b) 2.5^{-2}
c) 16^{-4}
d) $(1.5)^{-1}$

e) $5^{\frac{1}{2}}$
f) $6^{\frac{1}{3}}$
g) $9^{\frac{1}{5}}$
h) $(4.2)^{\frac{2}{3}}$

i) $(1\frac{1}{4})^{-3}$
j) $(2\frac{3}{5})^{\frac{1}{5}}$
k) $(5\frac{1}{3})^{-2}$
l) $(10\frac{5}{6})^{\frac{5}{6}}$

Remember — fractional powers mean roots.

Q12
a) $\sqrt{(1.4)^2 + (0.5)^2}$

b) $5.9\left[(2.3)^{\frac{1}{4}} + (4.7)^{\frac{1}{2}}\right]$

c) $2.5 - 0.6[(7.1)^{-3} - (9.5)^{-4}]$

d) $(8.2)^{-2} + (1.6)^4 - (3.7)^{-3}$

e) $\dfrac{3\sqrt{8} - 2}{6}$

f) $\dfrac{15 + 3\sqrt{4.1}}{2.4}$

g) $3\sqrt{4.7} - 4\sqrt{2.1}$

h) $\dfrac{(2\frac{1}{4})^{-2} - (3\frac{1}{2})^{\frac{1}{2}}}{4.4}$

Q13
a) $\left(2\frac{1}{4}\right)^3 - (1.5)^2$

b) $(3.7)^{-2} + (4\frac{1}{5})^{\frac{1}{4}}$

c) $\sqrt[3]{5\frac{1}{3}} \times (4.3)^{-1}$

d) $(7.4)^{\frac{1}{3}} \times (6\frac{1}{4})^3$

e) $\dfrac{\sqrt{22\frac{1}{2}} + (3.4)^2}{(6.9)^3 \times 3.4}$

f) $\dfrac{(15\frac{3}{5})^2 \times (2.5)^{-3}}{3 \times 4\frac{1}{4}}$

g) $5[(4.3)^2 - (2.5)^{\frac{1}{2}}]$

h) $\dfrac{3.5(2\frac{1}{6} - \sqrt{4.1})}{(3.5)^2 \times (3\frac{1}{2})^{-2}}$

i) $\dfrac{1\frac{1}{2} + \frac{1}{4}[(2\frac{2}{3})^2 - (1.4)^2]}{(3.9)^{-3}}$

j) $\sqrt[3]{2.73} + 5\sqrt{2}$

Q14 Evaluate the following **without using a calculator**:

a) $8^{\frac{1}{3}}$

b) $49^{\frac{1}{2}}$

c) 3^{-2}

d) 4^{-3}

e) $64^{\frac{3}{2}}$

f) $16^{\frac{3}{4}}$

g) $27^{-\frac{1}{3}}$

h) $\left(\frac{81}{25}\right)^{-\frac{1}{2}}$

> When a fractional power has a numerator
> bigger than 1, it's often easier to do the root
> part before the power part, like this:
> $$4^{\frac{3}{2}} = \left(4^{\frac{1}{2}}\right)^3 = \left(\sqrt{4}\right)^3 = 2^3 = 8$$

Multiplying Out Brackets

Q1 Multiply out the brackets and simplify where possible:

a) $4(x + y - z)$

b) $x(x + 5)$

c) $-3(x - 2)$

d) $7(a + b) + 2(a + b)$

e) $3(a + 2b) - 2(2a + b)$

f) $4(x - 2) - 2(x - 1)$

g) $4e(e + 2f) + 2f(e - f)$

h) $14(2m - n) + 2(3n - 6m)$

i) $4x(x + 2) - 2x(3 - x)$

j) $3(2 + ab) + 5(1 - ab)$

k) $(x^2 - 2y)z - 2x^2(x + z)$

l) $4(x^2 - 2y) - (5 + x^2 - 2y)$

m) $a - 4(a + b)$

n) $4pq(2 + r^3) + 5qr^3(2p + 7)$

o) $x^2(x + 1)$

p) $4x^2\left(x + 2 + \dfrac{1}{x}\right)$

q) $8ab(a^3 + 3 + b)$

r) $7pq\left(p + q - \dfrac{1}{p}\right)$

s) $4[(x + y) - 3(y - x)]$

> Remember <u>FOIL</u> for multiplying double brackets —
> you don't want to miss any terms now, do you...

Q2 Multiply out the brackets and simplify your answers where possible:

a) $(x - 3)(x + 1)$

b) $(x - 3)(x + 5)$

c) $(x + 10)(x + 3)$

d) $(x - 5)(x - 2)$

e) $(x + 2)(x - 7)$

f) $(4 - x)(7 - x)$

g) $(2 + 3x)(3x - 1)$

h) $(3x + 2)(2x - 4)$

i) $(x - \sqrt{2})(4x + \sqrt{2})$

j) $2(2x + y)(x - 2y)$

k) $4(x + 2y)(3x - 2y)$

l) $(3x + 2y)^2$

m) $(2a - b)^2$

n) $(t - 2\sqrt{2})(t + 2\sqrt{2})$

o) $(3p + \sqrt{2})^2$

Q3 Find the product of $5x - 2$ and $3x + 2$.

Q4 Find the square of $2x - 1$.

> For triple brackets, use FOIL on
> two of the brackets, then multiply
> the result by the third bracket.

Q5 Multiply out the brackets and simplify your answers where possible.

a) $(x + 1)(x - 2)(x + 2)$

b) $(x + 3)(x + 2)(x + 5)$

c) $(x - 2)(2x - 1)(x - 5)$

d) $(3 - x)(2 + x)(5 + x)$

e) $(1 - 2x)(1 + x)(3 + x)$

f) $(x + 10)(4 + 2x)(1 + 3x)$

g) $(3 + x)^2(3 - x)$

h) $(x - 1)(2x + 1)^2$

i) $(x + 3)^3$

Q6 A rectangular pond has length $(3x - 2)$ m and width $(5 - x)$ m.
Write down a simplified expression for:

a) the pond's perimeter

b) the pond's area

Q7 A rectangular bar of chocolate consists of 20
small rectangular pieces. The size of each
small rectangular piece is 2 cm by x cm.

a) The bar is broken up into its 20 separate pieces.
Write down an expression for the perimeter of one piece.

b) Write down an expression for the sum of the perimeters of all 20 pieces.
Give your answer in the form $(ax + b)$ cm.

Q8 Find a simplified expression for the perimeter <u>and</u> the area of the following shapes.

a)

b)

c)

d)

Factorising

Factorising means putting brackets in — you need to look for common factors in all the terms and put them outside a bracket, then put whatever's left inside the bracket.

Q1   All the expressions below have a^2 as a common factor. Factorise each of them.

a) $a^2b + a^2c$

b) $5a^2 + 13a^2b$

c) $2a^2b + 3a^2c$

d) $a^3 + a^2y$

e) $2a^2x + 3a^2y + 4a^2z$

f) $a^2b^2 + a^3c^2$

Q2   Factorise the following expressions.

a) $x^2 - 5x$

b) $2x + 6$

c) $3x^2 + 12x$

d) $4x^2 - 6x$

e) $3xy + 12x^2y$

f) $9x + 15$

g) $15x^2y - 25x$

h) $4pq^2 - 20pq + 8p^2q$

i) $10x^4 + 6x$

j) $15x^3 - 20x^2$

k) $21x^2 + 14x$

l) $5xyz + 20uxy$

Q3   Factorise the following:

a) $4x + 8xyz$

b) $8x^3y + 12x^2z$

c) $8xyz + 16x^2yz$

d) $20x^2y^2z^2 + 16xyz^2$

Q4   Using the fact that $a^2 - b^2 = (a + b)(a - b)$, factorise the following expressions.

a) $x^2 - 9$

b) $y^2 - 16$

c) $25 - z^2$

d) $36 - a^2$

e) $4x^2 - 9$

f) $9y^2 - 4$

g) $25 - 16z^2$

h) $1 - 36a^2$

i) $x^4 - 36$

j) $x^4 - y^4$

k) $1 - (ab)^2$

l) $100x^2 - 144y^2$

Q5   Factorise:

a) $x^2 - 4$

b) $144 - y^4$

c) $1 - 9x^2y^2$

d) $49x^4y^4 - 1$

e) $3x^2 - 12$

f) $90 - 10y^2$

g) $50x^2 - 32$

h) $20 - 45x^2y^2$

Q6   Factorise the following expressions, giving each answer in the form $(a + b)(a - b)$.

a) $x^2 - 3$

b) $9x^2 - 5$

c) $x^2 - 7y^2$

d) $2 - (xy)^2$

> Remember, you can rewrite a non-square number like this:
> $$11 = \left(\sqrt{11}\right)^2$$

These questions are a mixed bunch so look out for which ones are D.O.T.S. and which ones aren't.

Q7   Factorise the following expressions.

a) $64a^2b^3 - 16b^2a^3$

b) $pq + qr - pq^2r$

c) $3m^2 - 24$

d) $b^4 - ab^3 + b^2c$

e) $a^4 - 169$

f) $9ab^2 - 3abc$

g) $81 - z^2$

h) $121p^2 - 9q^2$

i) $m^2n + 3mn - 2mn^3$

j) $72m^2 - 50n^2$

k) $144x^2 - 108y^2 - 60z^2$

l) $64a^2b^2 - 49c^2d^2$

Manipulating Surds

Do these questions **without** using a calculator.
They're actually not as bad as they might look because you can leave √ or π in your answer.

Q1 Simplify:

a) $\sqrt{5} \times \sqrt{3}$ b) $\dfrac{\sqrt{20}}{\sqrt{5}}$ c) $\left(\sqrt{x}\right)^2$

d) $\sqrt{x^2}$ e) $\sqrt{8} \times \sqrt{8}$ f) $\dfrac{\sqrt{30}}{\sqrt{6}}$

Remember...
no calculators
on this page.

Q2 A circle has radius $\sqrt{3}$ cm. What is its exact area? (Area of circle $= \pi r^2$.)

Q3 Simplify these expressions:

Remember — $\sqrt{a} \times \sqrt{b} = \sqrt{(ab)}$.

a) $\sqrt{4} - \sqrt{1}$ b) $2\sqrt{3} + 3\sqrt{3}$ c) $\sqrt{8}$ d) $\left(2 + \sqrt{3}\right)^2$

e) $4\sqrt{5} - \sqrt{5}$ f) $\sqrt{50}$ g) $\sqrt{8} - \sqrt{2}$ h) $\sqrt{18} - \sqrt{9}$

Q4 Rationalise the denominators of the following expressions, and then simplify if necessary.

a) $\dfrac{2}{\sqrt{8}}$ b) $\dfrac{a}{\frac{\sqrt{40}}{2}}$ c) $\dfrac{x}{\sqrt{xy}}$ d) $\dfrac{6}{3 + \sqrt{3}}$

e) $\dfrac{2}{1 + \sqrt{6}}$ f) $\dfrac{5 + \sqrt{5}}{5 - \sqrt{5}}$ g) $\dfrac{2 + 3\sqrt{3}}{3 - \sqrt{3}}$ h) $\dfrac{1 - 2\sqrt{6}}{2 - 3\sqrt{6}}$

Remember: rationalising the denominator means getting
rid of any square root signs on the bottom of the fraction.

Q5 Simplify these expressions:

a) $\sqrt{28} + \sqrt{63} + \sqrt{7}$ b) $\sqrt{2} \times \left(\sqrt{6}\right)^3 - \sqrt{48}$ c) $\sqrt{135} + \sqrt{3} \times \left(\sqrt{5}\right)^5$

d) $\dfrac{2}{\sqrt{3}} + \dfrac{5}{\sqrt{27}}$ e) $\dfrac{6}{\sqrt{28}} - \dfrac{9}{\sqrt{63}}$ f) $\dfrac{60}{\sqrt{20}} + \dfrac{90}{\sqrt{45}} - \sqrt{80}$

g) $\left(4 - 3\sqrt{3}\right)\left(2 + \sqrt{3}\right)$ h) $\left(1 + 2\sqrt{2}\right)^2$ i) $\dfrac{2}{1 + \dfrac{1}{\sqrt{3}}}$

Q6 Are the following expressions rational or irrational?

a) $(1 + \sqrt{5})(1 - \sqrt{5})$ b) $\dfrac{1 + \sqrt{5}}{1 - \sqrt{5}}$

Q7 If $x = 1$ and $y = \sqrt{2}$, are the following expressions rational or irrational?

a) $(x + y)(x - y)$ b) $\dfrac{x + y}{x - y}$

Solving Equations

Q1 When 1 is added to a number and the answer then trebled, it gives the same result as doubling the number and then adding 4. Find the number.

Q2 Solve the following.
   a) $3x + 1 = 2x + 6$ **c)** $5x - 1 = 3x + 19$ **e)** $11 - 3x = 3 - 5x$

   b) $4x + 3 = 3x + 7$ **d)** $x + 2 = \frac{1}{2}x - 1$ **f)** $3x - 15 = 15 - 2x$

Q3 Solve the following.
   a) $3x - 8 = 7$ **c)** $4(2x - 1) = 60$ **e)** $\frac{24}{x} + 2 = 6$

   b) $2(x - 3) = -2$ **d)** $2x - 9 = 25$ **f)** $5x - 2 = 6x - 7$

Q4 **(x + 1) cm**   A square has sides of length $(x + 1)$ cm. Find the value of x if:

      a) the perimeter of the square is 66 cm

      b) the perimeter of the square is 152.8 cm.

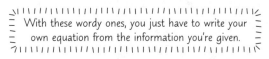

With these wordy ones, you just have to write your own equation from the information you're given.

Q5 Mrs Smith took her car to the local garage. She spent £x on new parts, four times this amount on labour and finally £29 for an MOT test. If the total bill was £106.50, find the value of x.

Q6 Solve:
   a) $2(x - 3) - (x - 2) = 5$ **f)** $3(7 + 2x) + 2(1 - x) = 19$ **i)** $41 - \frac{x}{11} = 35$

   b) $5(x + 2) - 3(x - 5) = 29$

   c) $2(x + 2) + 3(x + 4) = 31$ **g)** $\frac{x}{3} + 7 = 12$ **j)** $\frac{x}{100} - 3 = 4$

   d) $10(x + 3) - 4(x - 2) = 7(x + 5)$

   e) $5(4x + 3) = 4(7x - 5) + 3(9 - 2x)$ **h)** $\frac{x}{10} + 18 = 29$ **k)** $\frac{120}{x} = 16$

Q7 Joan, Kate and Linda win £2400 between them on the National Lottery. Joan gets a share of £x, whilst Kate gets twice as much as Joan. Linda's share is £232 less than Joan's amount.
   a) Write down an expression for the amounts Joan, Kate and Linda win.
   b) Write down an equation in terms of x, and solve it.
   c) Write down the amounts Kate and Linda receive.

Q8 The shape opposite is made up of two rectangles.
   a) Write down an expression for the perimeter of the shape.
   b) Write down an expression for the area of the shape.
   c) For what value of x will the perimeter and area be numerically equal?

Q9 Solve the following:
   a) $5(x - 1) + 3(x - 4) = -11$ **c)** $\frac{3x}{2} + 3 = x$ **e)** $\frac{5x + 7}{9} = 3$

   b) $3(x + 2) + 2(x - 4) = x - 3(x + 3)$ **d)** $3(4x + 2) = 2(2x - 1)$ **f)** $\frac{2x + 7}{11} = 3$

Solving Equations

Q10 For what value of x is the expression $14 - \frac{x}{2}$ equal to the expression $\frac{3x-4}{2}$?

It's easy — you just put the 2 bits together and there's your equation. Then all you've got to do is solve it...

Q11 Two men are decorating a room. One has painted 20 m² and the other only 6 m². They continue painting and manage to paint another x m² each. If the first man has painted exactly three times the area painted by the second man, find the value of x.

Q12 Carol's father was 24 years old when Carol was born. Now he is four times as old as Carol. How old is Carol?

Q13 Mr Jones is 4 years older than his wife and 31 years older than his son. All three ages add up to 82 years. If Mr Jones is x years old, find the value of x and find the ages of his wife and son.

Q14 A triangle has the side lengths shown below. Find the length of each side, if the length of AC exceeds that of AB by ½ cm.

Q15 Solve the following:

a) $\frac{y}{2} + 2 = 13$

b) $\frac{3x}{4} - 2 = 4$

c) $\frac{2z}{5} - 3 = -5$

d) $\frac{1}{5}(x - 4) = 3$

e) $\frac{2}{3}(x + 1) = 16$

f) $\frac{3}{5}(4x - 3) = 15$

g) $\frac{3x+2}{2} = 4x - 9$

h) $\frac{4x-5}{7} = 10 - 3x$

i) $\frac{13x+4}{10} = \frac{11x+5}{9}$

Q16 A train travels at 70 mph for x hours and then at 80 mph for $3\frac{3}{4}$ hours. If the train covers 405 miles of track, find the value of x.

Q17 Solve the following:

a) $\frac{5}{7}(x - 2) - \frac{3}{4}(x + 3) = -4$

Remember to do the same to the top and the bottom.

b) $\frac{2x-1}{3} - \frac{3x+5}{2} = -7$

c) $\frac{4x+7}{5} + \frac{5x+2}{4} = 6$

d) $\frac{4x+3}{2} + x = \frac{5x+41}{4}$

Q18 Solve the following:

a) $2x^2 = 18$
b) $2x^2 = 72$
c) $3x^2 = 27$
d) $4x^2 = 36$
e) $5x^2 = 5$

f) $2x^2 + 1 = 9$
g) $9x^2 - 3 = 1$
h) $16x^2 - 5 = 4$
i) $30 - \frac{x^2}{2} = 28$

j) $17 - \frac{x^2}{3} = 5$

k) $\frac{8}{x^2} = \frac{32}{36}$

l) $\frac{12}{5x^2} = \frac{3}{20}$

m) $\frac{14}{3x^2} = \frac{2}{21}$

Rearranging Formulas

Rearranging is getting the letter you want out of the formula and making it the subject. And it's (almost) the same method as for solving equations, which can't be bad.

Q1 Rearrange the following formulas to make the letter in brackets the new subject.

a) $g = 10 - 4h$ (h)

b) $d = \frac{1}{2}(c + 4)$ (c)

c) $j = -2(3 - k)$ (k)

d) $a = \frac{2b}{3}$ (b)

e) $f = \frac{3g}{8}$ (g)

f) $y = \frac{x}{2} - 3$ (x)

g) $s = \frac{t}{6} + 10$ (t)

h) $p = 4q^2$ (q)

Q2 Jason is saving up to go travelling next year and has got a temporary job selling cars. He is paid a basic wage of £500 a month, plus a bonus of £50 for each car he sells. He has a spreadsheet to keep track of his money, which calculates his wages (£w) after working for m months and selling c cars, using the following formula:
$$w = 500m + 50c$$
a) Rearrange the formula to make c the subject.
b) Find the number of cars Jason needs to sell in 11 months to earn £12 100.

Q3 The cost of hiring a car is £28 per day plus 25p per mile.
a) Find the cost of hiring the car for a day and travelling:
  i) 40 miles
  ii) 80 miles
b) Write down a formula to give the cost (£c) of hiring a car for one day and travelling n miles.
c) Rearrange the formula to make n the subject.
d) Find the number of miles you can travel during one day if you have a budget of:
  i) £34   **ii)** £50   **iii)** £56.50

You can get rid of square root signs by squaring both sides of the equation.

Q4 Rearrange the following formulas to make the letter in brackets the new subject.

a) $y = x^2 - 2$ (x)

b) $y = \sqrt{(x + 3)}$ (x)

c) $r = \left(\frac{s}{2}\right)^2$ (s)

d) $f = \frac{10 + g}{3}$ (g)

e) $w = \frac{5 - z}{2}$ (z)

f) $v = \frac{1}{3}x^2 h$ (x)

g) $v^2 = u^2 + 2as$ (a)

h) $v^2 = u^2 + 2as$ (u)

i) $t = 2\pi\sqrt{\frac{l}{g}}$ (g)

Q5 Mrs Smith buys x jumpers for £J each and sells them in her shop for a total price of £T.
a) Write down an expression for the amount of money she paid for all the jumpers.
b) Using your answer to **a)**, write down a formula for the profit £P Mrs Smith makes selling all the jumpers.
c) Rearrange the formula to make J the subject.
d) Given that Mrs Smith makes a profit of £156 by selling 13 jumpers for a total of £364, find the price she paid for each jumper originally.

Rearranging Formulas

Q6 A website offering digital photo printing charges 12p per print plus 60p postage.
a) Find the cost of ordering:
  i) 12 prints
  ii) 24 prints
b) Write down a formula for the cost C, in pence, of ordering x prints.
c) Rearrange the formula to make x the subject.
d) A regular customer is looking through old receipts to check she has been charged the right amount. Find the number of prints she should have received in each of her last three transactions if she was charged:
  i) £4.92
  ii) £6.36
  iii) £12.12

Q7 Rearrange the following to make x the subject.
a) $xy = z - 2x$
b) $ax = 3x + b$
c) $4x - y = xz$
d) $xy = 3z - 5x + y$

e) $xy = xz - 2$
f) $2(x - y) = z(x + 3)$
g) $xyz = x - y - wz$
h) $3y(x + z) = y(2z - x)$

> Start by collecting terms containing x on the same side of the equals sign.

> You'll need to get rid of any fractions before you start collecting all the terms involving the subject.

Q8 Rearrange the following to make y the subject.

a) $x(y - 1) = y$

b) $x(y + 2) = y - 3$

c) $x = \dfrac{y + 3}{2y - 5}$

d) $x + 1 = \dfrac{3y + 7}{5y + 2}$

e) $x = \dfrac{y^2 + 1}{2y^2 - 1}$

f) $x = \dfrac{2y^2 + 1}{3y^2 - 2}$

Q9 Rearrange the following to make the letter in brackets the subject.

a) $pq = 3p + 4r - 2q$ $\quad (p)$

b) $fg + 2e = 5 - 2g$ $\quad (g)$

c) $a(b - 2) = c(b + 3)$ $\quad (b)$

d) $pq^2 = rq^2 + 4$ $\quad (q)$

e) $4(a - b) + c(a - 2) = ad$ $\quad (a)$

f) $\dfrac{x^2}{3} - y = x^2$ $\quad (x)$

g) $\sqrt{hk^2 - 14} = k$ $\quad (k)$

h) $2\sqrt{x} + y = z\sqrt{x} + 4$ $\quad (x)$

i) $\dfrac{a}{b} = \dfrac{1}{3}(b - a)$ $\quad (a)$

j) $\dfrac{m + n}{m - n} = \dfrac{3}{4}$ $\quad (m)$

k) $\sqrt{\dfrac{(d - e)}{e}} = 7$ $\quad (e)$

l) $\dfrac{x - 2y}{xy} = 3$ $\quad (y)$

Factorising Quadratics

Q1 Solve these quadratic equations by factorising.

a) $x^2 + 3x - 10 = 0$

b) $x^2 - 5x + 6 = 0$

c) $x^2 - 2x + 1 = 0$

d) $x^2 - 4x + 3 = 0$

e) $x^2 - x - 20 = 0$

f) $x^2 + 14x + 49 = 0$

g) $-x^2 - x + 12 = 0$

h) $-x^2 - 7x + 8 = 0$

i) $-x^2 + 2x + 35 = 0$

Q2 Solve the following quadratic equations by factorising.

a) $2x^2 - 3x - 5 = 0$

b) $3x^2 + 4x - 7 = 0$

c) $2x^2 - 7x - 15 = 0$

d) $4x^2 + 12x + 9 = 0$

e) $4x^2 + 7x - 2 = 0$

f) $5x^2 - 31x + 6 = 0$

g) $-3x^2 - x + 2 = 0$

h) $-2x^2 + 9x - 10 = 0$

i) $-9x^2 - 3x + 2 = 0$

Q3 Rearrange into the form "$ax^2 + bx + c = 0$", then solve by factorising.

a) $x^2 + 6x = 16$

b) $x^2 + 5x = 36$

c) $x^2 + 4x = 45$

d) $x^2 = 5x$

e) $x^2 = 11x$

f) $x^2 - 21 = 4x$

g) $x^2 - 300 = 20x$

h) $x^2 + 48 = 26x$

i) $x^2 + 36 = 13x$

j) $x + 5 - \dfrac{14}{x} = 0$

k) $x + 4 - \dfrac{21}{x} = 0$

l) $x(3x + 1) = 10$

m) $2x^2 - 9(x + 2) = 0$

n) $4x + \dfrac{25}{x} = 20$

o) $6x - 1 = \dfrac{12}{x}$

Q4 Solve $x^2 - \dfrac{1}{4} = 0$.

Q5 The area of a rectangular swimming pool is 28 m². The width is x m. The difference between the length and the width is 3 m. Find the value of x.

x m

Q6 A rectangular rug has length x m. The width is exactly 1 m less than the length.

— x m —

a) Write down an expression for the area of the rug.

b) If the area of the rug is 6 m², find the value of x.

Q7 A triangle has height $(x + 1)$ cm and a base of $2x$ cm.

a) Write down an expression for the area of the triangle and simplify it.

b) If the area of the triangle is 12 cm², find the value of x.

$(x + 1)$ cm

— 2x cm —

Q8 A square room has a floor with sides measuring x metres. The height of the walls is 3 m.

a) Write down an expression for:

  i) the floor area

  ii) the total area of all four walls

b) If the total area of the floor and the four walls is 64 m², form a quadratic equation and solve it to find x.

The Quadratic Formula

Oh, go on then, I'll tell you the quadratic formula just
this once, but only because I'm so kind — it's $x = \dfrac{-b \pm \sqrt{b^2 - 4ac}}{2a}$.
You won't be given the formula in the exam though, so get it learnt.

Q1   Find the two values, to 2 decimal places, given by each of the following expressions:

a) $\dfrac{2 \pm \sqrt{3}}{2}$

b) $\dfrac{4 \pm \sqrt{10}}{3}$

c) $\dfrac{-2 \pm \sqrt{27}}{2}$

d) $\dfrac{-3 \pm \sqrt{42}}{3}$

e) $\dfrac{-10 \pm \sqrt{160}}{5}$

f) $\dfrac{-27 \pm \sqrt{10}}{2}$

g) $\dfrac{-8 \pm \sqrt{9.5}}{2.4}$

h) $\dfrac{10 \pm \sqrt{88.4}}{23.2}$

Q2   The following quadratics can be solved by factorisation,
but practise using the formula to solve them.

a) $x^2 + 8x + 12 = 0$
b) $6x^2 - x - 2 = 0$
c) $x^2 - x - 6 = 0$
d) $x^2 - 3x + 2 = 0$
e) $4x^2 - 15x + 9 = 0$
f) $x^2 - 3x = 0$
g) $36x^2 - 48x + 16 = 0$
h) $3x^2 + 8x = 0$
i) $2x^2 - 7x - 4 = 0$

j) $x^2 + x - 20 = 0$
k) $4x^2 + 8x - 12 = 0$
l) $3x^2 - 11x - 20 = 0$
m) $x + 3 = 2x^2$
n) $5 - 3x - 2x^2 = 0$
o) $1 - 5x + 6x^2 = 0$
p) $3(x^2 + 2x) = 9$
q) $x^2 + 4(x - 3) = 0$
r) $x^2 = 2(4 - x)$

> Don't forget to rearrange the
> equation into the form
> $ax^2 + bx + c = 0$ if necessary.

Step number 1...
Write out the formula.

Step number 2...
Write down values for
a, b and c.

Step number 3...
Sub a, b and c into the formula. Make sure you divide
the whole of the top line by 2a — not just half of it.

Q3   Solve the following quadratics using the formula.
Give your answers to two decimal places.

a) $x^2 + 3x - 1 = 0$
b) $x^2 - 2x - 6 = 0$
c) $x^2 + x - 1 = 0$
d) $x^2 + 6x + 3 = 0$
e) $x^2 + 5x + 2 = 0$

f) $x^2 - x - 1 = 0$
g) $3x^2 + 10x - 8 = 0$
h) $x^2 + 4x + 2 = 0$
i) $x^2 - 6x - 8 = 0$
j) $x^2 - 14x + 11 = 0$

k) $x^2 + 3x - 5 = 0$
l) $7x^2 - 15x + 6 = 0$
m) $2x^2 + 6x - 3 = 0$
n) $2x^2 - 7x + 4 = 0$
o) $3x^2 + 11x + 9 = 0$

Oops, forgot to mention **step number 4...**
check your answers by putting them **back in the equation.**

The Quadratic Formula

Q4 Rearrange the following into the form "$ax^2 + bx + c = 0$" and then find the **exact** solutions by using the quadratic formula. Simplify your answers where possible.

a) $x^2 = 8 - 3x$

b) $(x + 2)^2 - 3 = 0$

c) $3x(x - 1) = 5$

d) $2x(x + 4) = 1$

e) $x^2 = 4(x + 1)$

f) $(2x - 1)^2 = 5$

g) $3x^2 + 2x = 6$

h) $(x + 2)(x + 3) = 5$

i) $(x - 2)(2x - 1) = 3$

j) $2x + \dfrac{4}{x} = 7$

k) $\left(x - \dfrac{1}{2}\right)^2 = \dfrac{1}{2}$

l) $4x(x - 3) = -3$

m) $3x - \dfrac{3}{x + 1} = -12$

n) $2x - \dfrac{1}{x + 2} = -2$

o) $1 + \dfrac{3}{x + 5} = \dfrac{3}{x + 2}$

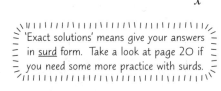
'Exact solutions' means give your answers in <u>surd</u> form. Take a look at page 20 if you need some more practice with surds.

Q5 The sides of a right-angled triangle are as shown. Use Pythagoras' theorem to form a quadratic equation in x and then solve it to find x.

Remember, for right-angled triangles, Pythagoras' theorem is:
$a^2 + b^2 = c^2$

2x cm

(2x + 2.4) cm

(x + 3) cm

Q6 The area of a rectangle with length $(x + 4.6)$ cm and width $(x - 2.1)$ cm is 134.63 cm².

a) Form a quadratic equation and solve it to find x to two decimal places.

b) What is the rectangle's perimeter to one decimal place?

Careful here — remember lengths have to be positive.

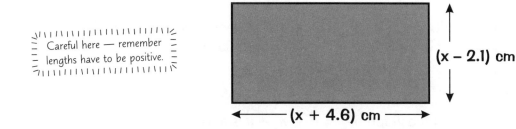

(x − 2.1) cm

(x + 4.6) cm

Completing the Square

All you're doing is writing quadratics in the form "(x + 4)² + 2" instead of "x² + 8x + 18" — don't let the name put you off.

Q1 Complete the square for the following expressions.

a) $x^2 - 4x - 5$

b) $x^2 - 2x + 1$

c) $x^2 + x + 1$

d) $x^2 - 6x + 9$

e) $x^2 - 6x + 7$

f) $x^2 - 4x$

g) $x^2 + 3x - 4$

h) $x^2 - x - 3$

i) $x^2 - 10x + 25$

j) $x^2 - 10x$

k) $x^2 + 8x + 17$

l) $x^2 - 12x + 35$

Q2 Solve the following quadratic equations by completing the square. Write down your answers correct to 2 d.p.

a) $x^2 + 3x - 1 = 0$

b) $x^2 - x - 3 = 0$

c) $x^2 + 4x - 3 = 0$

d) $x^2 + x - 1 = 0$

e) $x^2 - 3x - 5 = 0$

f) $2x^2 - 6x + 1 = 0$

g) $3x^2 - 3x - 2 = 0$

h) $3x^2 - 6x - 1 = 0$

> If you've got an ax^2, take out a factor of 'a' before completing the square, like this: $3x^2 + 12x + 1 = 3(x^2 + 4x) + 1$

Q3 Solve the following quadratic equations by completing the square. Give your answers as surds, simplifying where possible.

a) $x^2 - 8x - 13 = 0$

b) $x^2 - 2x - 5 = 0$

c) $x^2 + 6x - 11 = 0$

d) $x^2 + 8x + 4 = 0$

e) $x^2 + 3x - 2 = 0$

f) $x^2 + 7x + 3 = 0$

g) $x^2 - 5x - 25 = 0$

h) $x^2 - 9x + 9 = 0$

i) $2x^2 + 4x - 7 = 0$

j) $3x^2 - 6x - 1 = 0$

k) $-2x^2 + 7x + 3 = 0$

l) $-3x^2 + 5x - 1 = 0$

Q4 By completing the square, find the coordinates of the minimum point on the graph of each of the following equations.

a) $y = x^2 - 10x - 3$

b) $y = x^2 - 7x - 15$

> The minimum point occurs when the bracket in the completed square equals O.

c) $y = 3x^2 + 12x + 2$

d) $y = 4x^2 - 5x - 1$

Q5 By completing the square, find the coordinates of the turning point on the graph of each of the following equations. In each case, state whether the turning point is a maximum or a minimum.

a) $y = x^2 + 4x - 1$

b) $y = -x^2 + 11x - 6$

c) $y = -x^2 - 3x + 8$

d) $y = 2x^2 + 8x - 11$

e) $y = 2x^2 + 5x - 1$

f) $y = -3x^2 - 6x + 2$

Q6 For each of the following, sketch the graph of the equation and label the turning point and y-intercept with their coordinates.

a) $y = x^2 + 2x - 1$

b) $y = -x^2 + 3x + 2$

c) $y = 2x^2 - x - 5$

Q7 The turning point of the graph of $y = x^2 + mx + n$ is at $(1, -5)$. What are the values of m and n?

Algebraic Fractions

Multiplying and dividing algebraic fractions is just the same as multiplying and dividing normal fractions — to multiply you just multiply the tops and bottoms separately and to divide you just turn the second fraction upside down and then multiply. Simple.

Q1 Simplify the following by cancelling down where possible:

a) $\dfrac{27x^4y^2z}{9x^3yz^2}$ b) $\dfrac{48a^2b^2}{(2a)^2c}$ c) $\dfrac{3xyz}{9x^2y^3z^4}$ d) $\dfrac{4p^3q^3}{(2pr)^3}$

Q2 Multiply out the following, leaving your answers as simplified as possible:

a) $\dfrac{x^2}{y}\times\dfrac{2}{x^3}$ c) $\dfrac{30a^2b^2c^2}{7}\times\dfrac{21c^2}{ab^3}$ e) $\dfrac{2a^2}{3}\times\dfrac{9b}{a}\times\dfrac{2a^2b}{5}$

b) $\dfrac{10z^3}{xy}\times\dfrac{4x^3}{5z}$ d) $\dfrac{4}{x}\times\dfrac{x^3}{2}\times\dfrac{x}{10}$ f) $\dfrac{400d^4}{51e^5}\times\dfrac{102d^2e^4}{800e^2f}$

It helps if you can cancel some factors before multiplying.

Q3 Divide the following, leaving your answers as simplified as possible:

a) $\dfrac{4x^3}{y}\div\dfrac{2x}{y^2}$ c) $\dfrac{5x^3}{y}\div\dfrac{1}{y}$ e) $\dfrac{4x}{y^4z^4}\div\dfrac{2}{y^2z^3}$

b) $\dfrac{30x^3}{y^2}\div\dfrac{10x}{y}$ d) $\dfrac{16xyz}{3}\div\dfrac{4x^2}{9}$ f) $\dfrac{3m}{2n^2}\div\dfrac{m}{4n}$

Q4 Simplify the following:

a) $\dfrac{(p+q)}{r}\times\dfrac{3}{2(p+q)}$ b) $\left(\dfrac{a}{b}\div\dfrac{c}{d}\right)\times\dfrac{ac}{bd}$ c) $\left(\dfrac{mn}{l}\times\dfrac{m-l}{n^2}\right)\div\left(\dfrac{m}{l+m}\div\dfrac{l}{n}\right)$

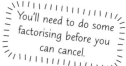
You'll need to do some factorising before you can cancel.

Q5 Simplify the following expressions:

a) $\dfrac{9a^2-16}{6a+8}$ c) $\dfrac{25x^2-36}{15x-18}$ e) $\dfrac{30a-5b}{36a^2-b^2}$

b) $\dfrac{4x^2-y^2}{8x+4y}$ d) $\dfrac{12x+21}{16x^2-49}$ f) $\dfrac{20x-12}{25x^2-9}$

Q6 Simplify the following:

a) $\dfrac{x^2-4}{x^2+x-6}$ b) $\dfrac{x^2+4x+3}{x^2-9}$ c) $\dfrac{x^2-25}{x^2+3x-10}$ d) $\dfrac{2x^2+9x+7}{4x^2-49}$

Algebraic Fractions

OK, I guess it gets a bit tricky here — you've got to get everything over a common denominator before you can get anywhere with adding or subtracting.

Q7   Express each of the following as a single fraction in its simplest form:

a) $\dfrac{6x}{3} + \dfrac{2x+y}{6}$

b) $\dfrac{x}{10} + \dfrac{y-1}{5}$

c) $\dfrac{x}{6} + \dfrac{5x}{7}$

d) $\dfrac{x}{8} + \dfrac{x+y}{4} + \dfrac{x-y}{2}$

e) $\dfrac{zx}{4} + \dfrac{x+z}{y}$

f) $\dfrac{m^2n}{p} + \dfrac{mn}{p^2}$

g) $\dfrac{2x+y}{x^2} + \dfrac{y}{x^3}$

h) $\dfrac{3}{x-4} + \dfrac{1}{x+2}$

i) $\dfrac{1}{x+y} + \dfrac{1}{x-y}$

j) $\dfrac{a+b}{a-b} + \dfrac{a-b}{a+b}$

k) $\dfrac{2x-9}{x+5} + \dfrac{x+1}{3x+4}$

l) $\dfrac{3x+1}{2x-3} + \dfrac{x-2}{2x+5}$

Q8   Express each of the following as a single fraction in its simplest form:

a) $\dfrac{z}{5} - \dfrac{2z}{15}$

b) $\dfrac{2b}{a} - \dfrac{b}{7}$

c) $\dfrac{p-2q}{4} - \dfrac{2p+q}{2}$

d) $\dfrac{2}{x} - \dfrac{3}{2x} - \dfrac{4}{3x}$

e) $\dfrac{3x}{y} - \dfrac{4-x}{3}$

f) $\dfrac{4}{a^2} - \dfrac{3b}{a+2}$

g) $\dfrac{x}{x+3} - \dfrac{1}{x-3}$

h) $\dfrac{3y}{x-1} - \dfrac{2y}{x+4}$

i) $\dfrac{y+1}{y^2} - \dfrac{y^2+1}{2y^3}$

j) $\dfrac{2}{3x-4} - \dfrac{4}{7x-2}$

k) $\dfrac{9}{4x-1} - \dfrac{2}{2x+3}$

l) $\dfrac{2x+3}{x-2} - \dfrac{x+2}{x+5}$

Q9   Simplify the following:

You'll need to factorise these before multiplying.

a) $\dfrac{2x+2}{y^2} \times \dfrac{xy}{x+1}$

b) $\dfrac{a^2}{a^2b+b^2} \times \dfrac{b^3+2b^2}{a^2b}$

c) $\dfrac{x+3}{x^2+3x-4} \times \dfrac{x-1}{x^2-9}$

d) $\dfrac{4x^2-25}{2x-8} \times \dfrac{2x+2}{2x^2-3x-5}$

e) $\dfrac{7x+21}{3x-3} \times \dfrac{2x^2-13x+11}{x^2+5x+6} \times (x^2-3x-10)$

f) $\dfrac{5x^2+30x+40}{3x^2+31x+36} \times \dfrac{7x+63}{x-1} \times \dfrac{3x^2+x-4}{4x^2+18x+8}$

Q10   Simplify the following:

a) $\dfrac{x-3}{y^2} \div \dfrac{2x^2y-6xy}{3}$

b) $\dfrac{4y^2}{x+1} \div \dfrac{1}{xy+y}$

c) $\dfrac{2x^2+x-3}{3x-3} \div \dfrac{4x^2y+8xy+3y}{5y}$

d) $\dfrac{7y}{2x^2y^2-5xy^2-12y^2} \div \dfrac{2}{2x^3+5x^2+3x}$

e) $\left(\dfrac{4x+24}{3x^2+36x+60} \div \dfrac{x-9}{2x+4}\right) \times (x^2+x-90)$

f) $\left(\dfrac{2x^2+14x+20}{x-1} \div \dfrac{x^2+2x-15}{x-2}\right) \div \dfrac{1}{x^2-4x+3}$

Sequences

Ahhh, sequences — you really need to know all about them and their nth terms.
They're a doddle once you figure out what's happening in each gap...

Q1 Write down the next three terms in each of these sequences and describe the sequence.

a) 2, 4, 6, 8, ...   c) 1, 4, 9, 16, ...

b) 1, 3, 5, 7, ...   d) 1, 8, 27, 64, ...

Q2 6   11   16   21   26 ...

a) What are the next three terms in this sequence?

b) What is the difference between each term?

c) Write down a formula for the nth term of this sequence.

d) Use the formula to find the 20th term of the sequence.

> It's easy to check your nth term formula — just put in a few values of n and check it gives you the sequence you started with.

Q3 Write down an expression for the nth term of the following sequences:

a) 2, 4, 6, 8, ...   b) 1, 3, 5, 7, ...   c) 5, 10, 15, 20, ...   d) 5, 8, 11, 14, ...

Q4 For the following sequences, write down the next three terms and the nth term:

a) 7, 10, 13, 16,...   b) 12, 17, 22, 27,...   c) 36, 26, 16, 6,...   d) 75, 68, 61, 54,...

Q5 A sequence is given by the rule **6n – 5**.
Is 53 a term in this sequence? Explain your answer.

Q6 1   5   9   13 ...

a) Find an expression for the nth term of this sequence.

b) Is 75 a term in this sequence? Explain your answer.

Q7 $\frac{1}{3}$ $\frac{2}{5}$ $\frac{3}{7}$ $\frac{4}{9}$ ...

> Treat the numerators and denominators as separate sequences.

a) What are the next three terms of this sequence?

b) Find an expression for the nth term of this sequence.

Q8 10, 20, 15, 17½, 16¼ ...

a) Write down the next four terms.   b) Explain how you would work out the 10th term.

Section Two — Algebra

Sequences

Q9 **3 3 6 9 15 24 ...**

  a) What is the rule for this sequence?
  b) Find the next three terms in the sequence.

Q10 **2 10 8 –2 –10 –8 ...**

  a) What are the next three terms of this sequence?
  b) What do you notice about how the sequence is behaving?
  c) What is the 20th term?

Q11 A sequence is given by the rule $u_{n+1} = u_n^2 - 5$.
  Given that $u_1 = 2$, find u_2 and u_3.

Remember, u_n means the nth term and u_{n+1} means the term after u_n.

Q12 Write down the next three terms of the following sequences:

  a) 5, 10, 20, 40, ...
  b) 1, 6, 36, 216, ...
  c) 0.1, 0.4, 1.6, 6.4, ...
  d) 729, 243, 81, 27, ...
  e) 31 250, 6250, 1250, 250, ...
  f) 12 288, 3072, 768, 192, ...
  g) 5103, 1701, 567, 189,...
  h) $1, \sqrt{3}, 3, 3\sqrt{3}, \ldots$
  i) $3, 3\sqrt{2}, 6, 6\sqrt{2}, \ldots$

Q13 State whether each of the following sequences is an arithmetic or geometric progression.
  Give the common difference or common ratio in each case.

  a) 1, 5, 9, 13, ...
  b) –25, –15, –5, 5 ...
  c) 2, 6, 18, 54, ...
  d) 9.6, 8.4, 7.2, 6, ...
  e) 20, 5, 1.25, 0.3125, ...
  f) 987, 876, 765, 654, ...

Q14 The nth term of a sequence is 5n + 10. The sum of two consecutive terms is 145.
  Find the values of these terms.

Q15 Write down the next three terms and the nth term of:

  a) 3, 9, 17, 27, ...
  b) 2, 3, 6, 11, ...
  c) 8, 16, 26, 38, ...
  d) 5, 21, 41, 65, ...
  e) 6, 11, 20, 33, ...
  f) 5, 18, 37, 62, ...

Q16 The nth term of a sequence is $3n^2 - 5$.
  Is 43 a term in this sequence? Explain your answer.

Q17

  The pattern above is based on individual triangles.

  a) Work out the number of individual triangles that would
    be in each of the next three groups.
  b) Find an expression for the number of triangles in the nth group.

Inequalities

Yet another one of those bits of Maths that looks worse than it is — these are just like equations, really, except for the symbols.

Q1 Write down the inequality represented by each diagram below.

a)

b)

c)

d)

e)

f)

Q2 Represent each of the following inequalities on a number line.
a) $x > 5$ c) $-5 < x < 2$ e) $-2 < x \le 3$ g) $-3 \le x \le -2$
b) $x \le 2$ d) $-2 \le x < 3$ f) $6 < x \le 7$ h) $-3 < x \le 0$

Q3 Given that x is an integer, find all the possible values of x satisfying the following inequalities. Write your answers using set notation.
a) $2 < x < 7$ b) $-2 \le x < 3$ c) $-5 \le x \le 0$

Q4 Solve the following:
a) $3x + 2 > 11$ e) $2x - 7 \ge 8$ i) $5(x + 2) \ge 25$ m) $8 - 3x \ge 14$
b) $5x + 4 < 24$ f) $17 + 4x < 33$ j) $4(x - 1) > 40$ n) $16 - x < 11$
c) $5x + 7 \le 32$ g) $2(x + 3) < 20$ k) $10 - 2x > 4x - 8$ o) $16 - x > 1$
d) $3x + 12 \le 30$ h) $2(5x - 4) < 32$ l) $7 - 2x \le 4x + 10$ p) $12 - 3x \le 18$

Q5 Solve the following:
a) $-2 < x - 3 < 5$ d) $7 < 4 - 3x \le 16$ g) $1 \le \frac{2x + 7}{3} < 5$
b) $1 \le x + 1 \le 9$ e) $2 \le \frac{x}{5} + 1 \le 3$ h) $-10 < \frac{x + 1}{5} \le -2$
c) $7 < 2x + 3 < 11$ f) $-2 < \frac{x - 3}{2} < 10$ i) $-1 \le \frac{2 - x}{3} < 6$

Section Two — Algebra

Inequalities

Q6   Find the largest integer x, such that $2x + 5 \geq 5x - 2$.

Q7   For each of the following pairs of inequalities, find the integer value of x which satisfies both of them.

a) $x - 3 > 2$ and $2x + 1 < 15$

c) $4 - x < 6$ and $\dfrac{x + 12}{3} < 4$

b) $3x - 11 > 19$ and $5x - 23 < 37$

d) $1 - 2x < 17$ and $\dfrac{2 - 3x}{10} > 2$

Q8   When a number is subtracted from 11, and this new number is then divided by two, the result is always less than five. Write this information as an inequality and solve it to show the possible values of the number.

Q9   Two schools are merging and a new school is being built to accommodate all the pupils. There will be 1130 pupils in total in the new school. No class can have more than 32 pupils.

a) Use this information to write down an inequality involving the number of classrooms, x, in the school.

b) What is the minimum number of classrooms that are needed?

Q10   A couple are planning their wedding. For the reception in a local hotel, they have a budget of £900 to spend on their guests. The hotel charges £18 per head.

a) Use this information to write down an inequality involving the number of guests.

b) What is the maximum number of guests that could be invited?

Q11   The shaded region in each of the following graphs satisfies three inequalities. Write down these inequalities.

> Remember, solid lines mean $\geq$ or $\leq$ and dotted lines mean $>$ or $<$.

a)

b)

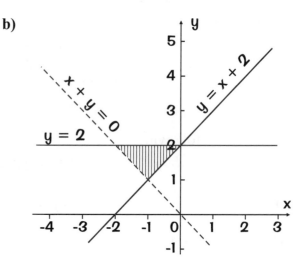

Inequalities

Q12 Draw a set of axes with the x-axis from -2 to 6 and the y-axis from -1 to 7. Show on a graph the region enclosed by the following three inequalities.

$$y < 6, \qquad x + y \geq 5 \qquad \text{and} \qquad x \leq 5$$

Q13 Draw a set of axes with the x-axis from -4 to 5 and the y-axis from -3 to 6. Show on a graph the region enclosed by the following.

$$y \leq 2x + 4, \qquad y < 4 - x \qquad \text{and} \qquad y \geq \frac{x}{3} - 1$$

Q14 A company are recruiting new members of staff. All applicants must take two online tests. To get an interview, applicants must score higher than 5 on the first test, at least 7 on the second, and have a total combined score of at least 14.

a) Write out three inequalities to represent the three criteria for getting an interview. Use x for the score on the first test and y for the score on the second test.

b) The company want to analyse the quality of applicants by plotting their test scores on a graph and picking out the ones who satisfy the criteria. Using suitable axes, show on a graph the region enclosed by the three inequalities where suitable candidates would be placed.

Q15 Solve the following:

a) $x^2 < 9$

b) $x^2 > 16$

c) $x^2 \leq 4$

d) $2x^2 \geq 18$

e) $x^2 \geq 25$

f) $2x^2 < 32$

g) $-x^2 < -36$

h) $-x^2 > -4$

i) $-3x^2 < -27$

j) $x^2 + 4 \leq 53$

k) $2x^2 - 5 > 45$

l) $17 - \dfrac{x^2}{3} < 5$

Q16 Write down the inequalities that the shaded region satisfies.

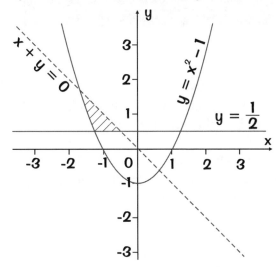

```
Sketching the graphs will help with these — if
you need some practice, have a look at page 46.
```

Q17 Solve the following:

a) $x^2 - x - 6 < 0$

b) $x^2 + 6x + 5 \leq 0$

c) $x^2 + 3x + 2 > 0$

d) $x^2 - 10x + 16 \geq 0$

e) $x^2 - 18 > 7x$

f) $12x + 35 < -x^2$

g) $-x^2 + 9x - 20 \leq 0$

h) $-x^2 - 2x + 3 > 0$

i) $2x^2 + 7x + 6 \leq 0$

j) $9x - 2x^2 < 4$

k) $3x^2 < x + 2$

l) $4x^2 + 11x \geq 20$

Iterative Methods

Iterative methods aren't as bad as they look (or sound) — all you're doing is repeating the same calculation with different values to home in on the solution.

Q1 The cubic equation $x^3 + x^2 - 4x = 3$ has three solutions. The first solution lies between −3 and −2. The second lies between −1 and 0. The third solution lies between 1 and 2. Copy the table below and use it to find all three solutions to 1 d.p.

Guess (x)	Value of $x^3 + x^2 - 4x$	Too large or Too small
−3	$(-3)^3 + (-3)^2 - 4(-3) = -6$	
−2	$(-2)^3 + (-2)^2 - 4(-2) =$	
−1	$(-1)^3 + (-1)^2 - 4(-1) =$	
0	$(0)^3 + (0)^2 - 4(0) =$	
1	$(1)^3 + (1)^2 - 4(1) =$	
2	$(2)^3 + (2)^2 - 4(2) =$	

Q2 The cubic equation $x^3 - 8x^2 - 3x + 9 = 0$ has three solutions. The first solution lies between −2 and −1. The second lies between 0 and 1. The third solution lies between 8 and 9. By using the decimal search method and a table like the one below, find each solution to 1 d.p.

x	Value of $x^3 - 8x^2 - 3x + 9$	Positive/Negative

Q3 The equation $x^3 - x^2 - 4x - 9 = 0$ has one solution. Use the iteration machine below to find this solution to 2 d.p. Use the starting value $x_0 = 3$.

1. Start with x_n →
2. Find the value of x_{n+1} by using the formula $x_{n+1} = \sqrt[3]{x_n^2 + 4x_n + 9}$. →
3. If $x_n = x_{n+1}$ rounded to 2 d.p. then stop. If $x_n \neq x_{n+1}$ rounded to 2 d.p. go back to step 1 and repeat using x_{n+1}.

Q4 Use the iteration machine below to find the three solutions to the equation $2x^3 - 5x + 1 = 0$ to 3 d.p. Use the starting values:

a) $x_0 = 0$ **b)** $x_0 = -2$ **c)** $x_0 = 2$

1. Start with x_n →
2. Find the value of x_{n+1} by using the formula $x_{n+1} = \dfrac{4x_n^3 - 1}{6x_n^2 - 5}$. →
3. If $x_n = x_{n+1}$ rounded to 3 d.p. then stop. If $x_n \neq x_{n+1}$ rounded to 3 d.p. go back to step 1 and repeat using x_{n+1}.

Simultaneous Equations

To solve simultaneous equations from scratch, you've got to get rid of
either x or y first — to leave you with an equation with just one unknown in it.

Q1 Solve the following simultaneous equations:

    a) $4x + 6y = 16$
       $x + 2y = 5$

    b) $3y - 8x = 24$
       $3y + 2x = 9$

    c) $3y - 10x - 17 = 0$
       $\frac{1}{3}y + 2x - 5 = 0$

    d) $\frac{x}{2} - 2y = 5$
       $12y + x - 2 = 0$

    e) $3x - 4y = 5x - 14$
       $2y + x = 11y - 26$

    f) $3x + 4y = 10$
       $5x - 7y = 3$

    g) $2y - 3x = 1$
       $4x + 5y = 37$

    h) $10x - 7y = -9$
       $8x + 9y = 22$

    i) $\frac{3}{5}x + 2y = 21$
       $2x - \frac{2}{3}y = 4$

Q2 Use the linear equation (the one with no x^2s in it) to find an expression for y. Then
substitute it into the quadratic equation (the one <u>with</u> x^2s in it), to solve these equations:

    a) $y = x^2 + 2$
       $y = x + 14$

    b) $y = x^2 - 8$
       $y = 3x + 10$

    c) $y = 2x^2$
       $x - y = -3$

    d) $y = x^2 - 2$
       $y - 3x = 8$

    e) $y = 3x^2 - 10$
       $13x - y = 14$

    f) $y + 2 = 2x^2$
       $2y + 6x = 0$

    g) $x + 5y = 30$
       $y - x^2 = \frac{4}{5}x$

    h) $y = 1 - 13x$
       $4x^2 + 4 - y = 0$

    i) $2y = 6(x^2 + 3)$
       $14x + y = 1$

    j) $x^2 + y^2 = 13$
       $y = x + 1$

    k) $x^2 + y^2 = 18$
       $y - x = 6$

    l) $y^2 - x^2 = 5$
       $4x - 2y = 2$

Q3 Two farmers are buying livestock at a market. Farmer Jill buys 6 sheep and 5 pigs
for £430 and Farmer Jacob buys 4 sheep and 10 pigs for £500.

    a) If sheep cost £x and pigs cost £y, write down the
two purchases as a pair of simultaneous equations.

    b) Solve for x and y.

Q4 On Farmer Palmer's farm, the cats have got into the chicken coop and are causing chaos.
Farmer Palmer counts, in total, 11 heads and 30 legs. How many cats and how many
chickens are in the chicken coop?

Q5 Find the values of x and y for each of the following rectangles by first writing down a pair
of simultaneous equations and then solving them.

Q6 Two customers enter a shop to buy milk and cornflakes. Mrs Smith buys 5 pints of milk
and 2 boxes of cornflakes and spends £3.44. Mr Brown buys
4 pints of milk and 3 boxes of cornflakes and receives £6.03
change after paying with a £10 note. Write down a pair of
simultaneous equations and solve them to find the price in
pence of a pint of milk (m) and a box of cornflakes (c).

Q7 Solve $\dfrac{3(x-y)}{5} = x - 3y = x - 6$.

Q8 Find the points of intersection of the curve $y = x^2 - 3x + 2$ and the line $y = 5 - x$.

Proof

Proofs look pretty scary but they're usually alright once you get started. For these first few questions you just need to do some rearranging and make one side of the identity look like the other side.

Q1 Prove that $(n + 3)^2 - (3n + 5) \equiv (n + 1)(n + 2) + 2$

Q2 Prove that $(n - 3)^2 - (n - 5) \equiv (n - 3)(n - 4) + 2$

Q3 Prove that $25 - \dfrac{(x - 8)^2}{4} \equiv \dfrac{(2 + x)(18 - x)}{4}$

Q4 Prove that if $3(ax + 7) - 2(x + b) \equiv 4x + 29$, then a = 2 and b = –4.

> Equate the coefficients here — write the coefficients of x equal to each other, and then the constants equal to each other.

Q5 Prove that $(2n + 1)^2 - (2n - 1)^2 - 10$ is not a multiple of 8 for positive integer values of n.

Q6 Prove that the sum of any three consecutive numbers is divisible by 3.

Q7 Prove that an even number multiplied by another even number will always result in an even number.

Q8 Prove that the sum of any three consecutive even numbers is always a multiple of 6.

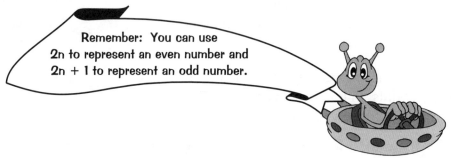

Remember: You can use 2n to represent an even number and 2n + 1 to represent an odd number.

Q9 Prove these statements.
a) The sum of any two consecutive odd numbers must be a multiple of 4.
b) The sum of the squares of any two consecutive odd numbers cannot be a multiple of 4.

You might have to prove that a statement isn't true.
The best way to do this is to find an example that doesn't work...

Q10 Maisy says "all prime numbers are odd". Prove that Maisy is wrong.

Q11 Prove that these statements are wrong.
a) If the sum of two integers is even, one of the integers must be even.
b) If n is an integer and n^2 is divisible by 4, then n is also divisible by 4.

Q12 Christine says "if $a^2 = b^2$, then a = b". Prove that Christine is wrong.

Proof

You'll need all kinds of maths tools to tackle these proofs — power rules, algebraic fractions, sequences... Don't panic if you're feeling stuck — you might need to experiment a bit before you find the right method.

Q13   Prove that $5^{20} - 5^{19}$ is even, without using a calculator.

Q14   Without using a calculator, prove that the sum of 21^8 and 15^4 is a multiple of 3.

Q15   Without using a calculator, prove that $3^8 - 1$ is not a prime number.

> Try thinking of this as a difference of two squares.

Q16   The nth term of a sequence is given by $\frac{1}{2}n^2 - \frac{5}{2}n + 3$.

Prove that the sum of any two consecutive numbers in the sequence is a square number.

Q17   If $a = 5^{99} \times 2^{98}$ and $b = 5^{72} \times 4^{38}$, show that ab has 172 digits when written as an ordinary number.

> Remember... $4 = 2^2$. Use this to write b as a power of 5 multiplied by a power of 2.

Q18   If $x > 0$, $y > 0$ and $x < y$, prove that $\dfrac{y^2 + 1}{y^2} - \dfrac{x^2 + 1}{x^2} < 0$.

Q19   The mean of a set of 6 numbers is 18.
If 1 is subtracted from each number in the set, show that the mean of the new set also decreases by 1.

> Remember — the mean is the sum of your set of values, divided by the number of values.

Q20   The nth term of a sequence is given by $n^2 - 2n + 2$.
Prove that the sum of any two consecutive numbers in the sequence is an odd number.

Q21   Fay claims that $x^2 + 3 > 2x + 1$ for all values of x.
Prove that Fay is correct.

> Try completing the square for this one...

Functions

Right, functions. Don't let appearances deceive you — treat them like the regular equations that you've seen loads of times before. Nothing to worry about here then.

Q1 Express this function machine using function notation.

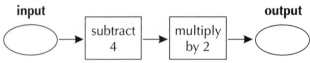

Q2 For the following functions find x when $f(x) = 2$:
a) $f(x) = 2x - 7$
b) $f(x) = 5 - 4x$
c) $f(x) = 3x - 10$
d) $f(x) = x^2 + 1$
e) $f(x) = x^2 + 7x$
f) $f(x) = 252 - 2x^3$

Q3 For the following functions find $f(5)$.
a) $f(x) = x + 4$
b) $f(x) = x^2 + x$
c) $f(x) = 18 - x^2 + 9x$
d) $f(x) = 65 \div x$
e) $f(x) = 121 \div 10x^2$
f) $f(x) = 4(x + x^3)$

Q4 If $f(x) = 4x + 12$ and $g(x) = 3 - x^2$ then find:
a) $f(8)$
b) $g(3)$
c) $f(x) + g(x)$
d) $f(2) - g(2)$
e) $f(-4)$
f) $gf(x)$
g) $fg(x)$
h) $gf(2)$

Q5 If $f(x) = 6 - 2x$, $g(x) = \dfrac{9}{x}$ and $h(x) = 6 + x^2$ then find:
a) $f(-1)$
b) $g(1/3)$
c) $hf(x)$
d) $gf(x)$
e) $fg(12)$
f) $hf(-9)$

Q6 If $f(x) = \dfrac{11}{x + 1}$, $g(x) = \dfrac{3x}{4}$ and $h(x) = 6 + x$ then find:
a) $h^{-1}(x)$
b) $f^{-1}(x)$
c) $h^{-1}(x) + f^{-1}(x)$
d) $f^{-1}(11) - h^{-1}(6)$
e) $g^{-1}(h(x))$
f) $f^{-1}(g(x))$
g) $h^{-1}(f(5))$
h) $h^{-1}(g(-1))$

Q7 Evaluate the following:
a) $f(-1)$ where $f(x) = \dfrac{2 + 4x}{3}$
b) $g(9)$ where $g(x) = 7x^2 - 13$
c) $kj(-3)$ where $j(x) = 3(x - 2)$ and $k(x) = -14x$
d) $n^{-1}(2)$ where $n(x) = 32 + 4(7 - x)$
e) $t^{-1}(3)$ where $t(x) = 21 + \dfrac{1}{2}(x + 3)$
f) $v^{-1}(r(2))$ where $v(x) = -\dfrac{x}{4}$ and $r(x) = 2x$

Q8 Find:
a) $fg(x)$, if $f(x) = 2x^3$ and $g(x) = 7 - x$
b) $m^{-1}(x)$, if $m(x) = \dfrac{9x - 6}{5}$
c) $p^{-1}(q(x))$, if $p(x) = 8x + 5$ and $q(x) = \dfrac{13}{x - 2}$

Q9 A function machine is shown below.

Find the range of input values for which the output is greater than the input.

Straight Lines and Gradients

Gradients might seem confusing at first, but remember — they're just 'the change in y' divided by 'the change in x'. Oh, and careful with those signs...

Q1   Which letters represent the following lines:

a) $x = y$
b) $x = 5$
c) $y = -x$
d) $x = 0$
e) $y = -5$
f) $x + y = 0$
g) $y = 5$
h) $x - y = 0$
i) $y = 0$
j) $x = -7$?

Don't get confused if you've got something like "$x + y = ...$" — just rearrange to get y on its own.

Q2   Find the gradient of:
a) line A
b) line B
c) line C
d) line D
e) line E
f) line F
g) line G
h) line H
i) line I
j) line J

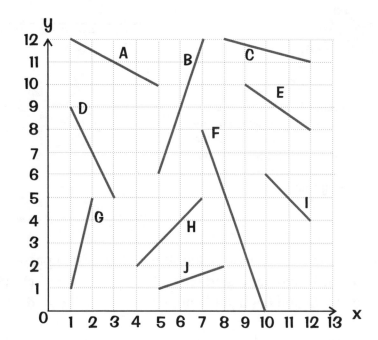

Q3   What is the gradient of the line joining the points:

a) (3, 5) and (5, 9)
b) (6, 3) and (10, 5)
c) (-6, 4) and (-3, 1)

d) (8, 2) and (4, 10)
e) (8, 5) and (6, 4)
f) (-3, -1) and (1, -4)?

Uphill gradients are always positive, downhill always negative. Impressed? Hmmm....thought not. Can be a bit of an uphill battle, these.

Q4   A straight line has gradient $-\frac{1}{3}$ and passes through the points (2, 3), (a, 2) and (11, b). What are the values of a and b?

y = mx + c

Writing the equation of a line in the form y = mx + c gives you a nifty way of finding the gradient and y-intercept. Remember that — it'll save you loads of time. Anything for an easy life...

Q1 For each of the following lines, give the gradient and the coordinates of the point where the line cuts the *y*-axis.

a) $y = 4x + 3$
b) $y = 3x - 2$
c) $y = 2x + 1$
d) $y = -3x + 3$

e) $y = 5x$
f) $y = -2x + 3$
g) $y = -6x - 4$
h) $y = x$

i) $y = -\frac{1}{2}x + 3$
j) $y = \frac{1}{4}x + 2$

k) $3y = 4x + 6$

I know these are a bit algebra-ish, but don't worry, they won't bite.

Q2 Find the equations of the following lines:

a) A
b) B
c) C
d) D
e) E
f) F

Yeah, OK, this sounds a bit scary, but just work out the gradient (m) and look at the y-intercept (c) and pop them back into "y = mx + c"... easy lemons.

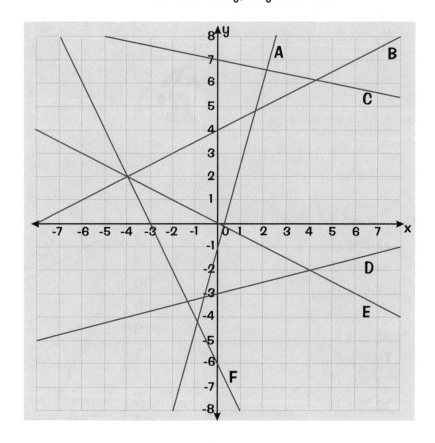

Q3 Find the equation of the straight line which passes through:
a) (3, 7) and has a gradient of 1
b) (2, 8) and has a gradient of 3
c) (4, -4) and has a gradient of -1
d) (-1, 7) and has a gradient of -3.

Q4 Write down the equation of the line which passes through the points:
a) (2, 2) and (5, 5)
b) (1, 3) and (4, 12)
c) (1, 0) and (5, -12)
d) (-5, 6) and (-1, -2).

Q5 Find the value of letters *a-d*, given that:
a) the point $(a, 13)$ is on the line $y = 3x + 1$
b) the point $(b, -2)$ is on the line $y = \frac{1}{2}x - 6$
c) the point $(4, c)$ is on the line $y = 2x - 1$
d) the point $(-3, d)$ is on the line $y = -3x$?

Q6 Which of the following points lie on the line $y = 3x - 1$?
(7, 20), (6, 15), (5, 14)

Section Three — Graphs

Drawing Straight Line Graphs

If you know it's a straight line, you only really need two points, but it's always a good idea to plot three — it's a bit of a safety net, really.

Q1 Complete this table of values for $y = 2x + 3$:

x	0	3	8
y			

Plot these points on graph paper and draw the graph of $y = 2x + 3$.
Use your graph to find:

a) The value of y when $x = 5$

b) The value of y when $x = 2$

c) The value of x when $y = 11$

d) The value of x when $y = 17$

Q2 Complete this table of values for $y = \frac{1}{4}x - 3$:

x	-8	-4	8
y			

Don't forget — you should always label your line with its equation.

Plot these points on graph paper and draw the graph of $y = \frac{1}{4}x - 3$.
Use your graph to find:

a) The value of y when $x = 2$

b) The value of y when $x = 0$

c) The value of x when $y = -2$

d) The value of x when $y = -1.5$

Q3 For each of the following, identify the <u>gradient</u> and <u>y-intercept</u> of the line.
Then use them to draw the graph of the given line on graph paper.

a) $y = 3x + 1$

b) $y = \frac{1}{2}x - 5$

c) $y = -3x + 4$

d) $y = -x - 1$

Q4 A line has the equation $2x - 3y = 8$.

a) Rearrange the equation into the form $y = mx + c$.

b) What are the coordinates of the point where the line cuts the y-axis?

c) What is the gradient of the line?

d) Use your answers to **b)** and **c)** to help you draw the line $2x - 3y = 8$ on graph paper.

Q5 Sketch the graphs of the following equations:

a) $y = 2x - 3$

b) $2y - x = 1$

c) $y = 3x - 6$

d) $4x + y = 8$

e) $x = 7 - y$

f) $2 + 2y = 9x$

When you're asked to <u>sketch</u> a line, it doesn't need to be super-accurate (so you <u>don't</u> need graph paper). But try to make the <u>gradient</u> roughly correct, and give the coordinates of <u>key points</u>, such as the x- and y-intercepts.

Q6 Draw the lines $y = \frac{1}{2}x + 1$ and $y = 2x - 2$ on graph paper.
Write down the coordinates of the point where the two lines intersect.

Coordinates and Ratio

Q1 Find the midpoint of the line AB, where A and B have coordinates:

    a) A(2, 3) B(4, 5)   **d)** A(6, 7) B(0, 0)

    b) A(0, 11) B(11, 11)   **e)** A(16, 16) B(3, 3)

    c) A(3, 15) B(14, 3)   **f)** A(17, 28) B(44, 13)

Your answers should be coordinates too.

ahh... nice'n'easy...

Q2 Anna is designing the plan of a kitchen using some computer aided design software. The coordinates of the room on screen are (0, 10), (220, 10), (0, 260), (220, 260). She needs to enter the coordinates of the ceiling light, which will be exactly in the centre of the room. What will the coordinates of the light be?

Q3 Find the midpoint of each of these lines:

    a) Line PQ, where P has coordinates (-1, 5) and Q has coordinates (5, 6).

    b) Line AB, where A has coordinates (-3, 3) and B has coordinates (4, 0).

    c) Line RS, where R has coordinates (4, -5) and S has coordinates (0, 0).

    d) Line GH, where G has coordinates (10, 13) and H has coordinates (-6, -7).

    e) Line MN, where M has coordinates (-5, -8) and N has coordinates (-21, -17).

Q4 Point Q lies on the line segment RS. Find the coordinates of Q when the coordinates of R and S and the ratio RQ : QS are as follows:

    a) R(2, 4) S(8, 10)   RQ:QS=1:2

    b) R(-4, 2) S(16, 17)   RQ:QS=3:2

    c) R(9, -1) S(-9, 3)   RQ:QS=1:3

    d) R(-21, -45) S(-14, -10)   RQ:QS=6:1

    e) R(7, -8) S(21, -7)   RQ:QS=3:1

    f) R(-17, 0) S(7, -17)   RQ:QS=3:5

Divide the horizontal distance between R and S in the given ratio — this will help you find the x-coordinate of Q. Then do the same thing with the vertical distance to find the y-coordinate of Q.

Q5 Point C lies on the line segment AB, with AC : CB = 2 : 7. Point A has coordinates (5, 3) and point C has coordinates (-1, 0). Find the coordinates of B.

Q6 On the graph on the right, G lies on the line segment DE, with DG : GE = 3 : 1. F and H lie on the circumference of the circle, and FH is a diameter of the circle.

    a) Find the coordinates of G.

    b) Is point G at the centre of the circle? Explain your answer.

Don't forget — the diameter of a circle goes through its centre.

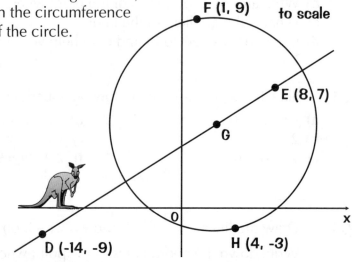

Parallel and Perpendicular Lines

When lines are parallel, their gradients are the same. When lines are perpendicular, their gradients multiply together to give -1. That's it — not much else to it really...

Q1 Identify whether each of the following pairs of straight lines are parallel, perpendicular or neither.

You only need to compare the gradients to answer this question.

a) $y = 3x + 4$, $y = 3x - 8$

b) $2y = x - 17$, $y = \frac{1}{2}x + 17$

c) $y = x - 4$, $y = -2x - 4$

d) $3y + 3x = 9$, $y = x + \frac{3}{2}$

e) $2x = y + 8$, $2y = x + 8$

f) $3 - x = 3y$, $y - 3x = 5$

g) $4y + 5x = 0$, $2y = 22 - \frac{5}{2}x$

h) $y = 2x - 8$, $8y + 4x = 9$

Q2 Line A has the equation $y = 3x - 4$.
Line B is parallel to line A and passes through (8, 25).

a) Find the gradient of line B.

b) Find the equation for line B.

Q3 Line C is defined by $y = \frac{1}{2}x + 12$.
Line D is perpendicular to line C and passes through (5, -13).

a) Find the gradient of line D.

b) Find the equation for line D.

Q4 Find the equation of the line which is:

a) parallel to $y = 2x - 1$ and passes through (4, 11).

b) perpendicular to $y = -\frac{1}{4}x + 1$ and passes through (5, 21).

c) parallel to $y = x$ and passes through (-2, -10).

d) parallel to $3y + 2x = 1$ and passes through (9, 0).

e) perpendicular to $10y + 5x = 3$ and passes through (-7, -1).

f) parallel to $8y - x + 4 = 0$ and passes through $(3, \frac{1}{2})$.

g) perpendicular to $2x = 8 - y$ and passes through (16, 47).

h) perpendicular to $6 + 8y = 3x$ and passes through (12, -37)

Q5 In each graph below, the position of one of the points on line A has been given. Find the equation of line A.

a)

b)

c)

Quadratic Graphs

 So, you can spot a quadratic graph at ten paces, but can you draw one...

Q1 Complete this table of values for the quadratic graph $y = 2x^2$.

a) Draw axes with x from -4 to 4 and y from 0 to 32.

b) Plot these 9 points and join them with a smooth curve.

c) Label your graph.

x	-4	-3	-2	-1	0	1	2	3	4
$y=2x^2$	32	18					8		

Q2 Complete this table of values for the graph $y = x^2 + 3x + 5$.

x	-4	-3	-2	-1	0	1	2	3
x^2	16	9					4	
$3x$				-3				9
$y=x^2+3x+5$	9					9		

a) Draw axes with x from -4 to 3 and y from 0 to 25.

b) Plot the points and join them with a smooth curve.

c) Draw and label the line of symmetry for the quadratic graph $y = x^2 + 3x + 5$.

If the x^2 term has a <u>minus</u> sign in front of it, the curve will be turned <u>upside down</u>.

Q3 Complete this table of values for the graph $y = 3 - x^2$.

a) Draw the graph $y = 3 - x^2$ for x from -4 to 4.

b) State the maximum y-value of the graph $y = 3 - x^2$.

x	-4	-3	-2	-1	0	1	2	3	4
$-x^2$	-16						-4		
$y=3-x^2$	-13						-1		

Q4 The curve on the right has the equation $y = ax^2 + bx + c$.

a) Find the value of c.

b) Write down the coordinates of the turning point.

c) Find the roots of the equation $ax^2 + bx + c = 0$.

Finding the roots of $ax^2 + bx + c = 0$ is just a fancy way of saying "what values of x give y = 0?"

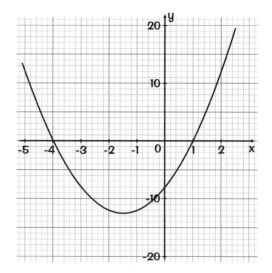

Q5 Sketch the following graphs. Make sure you label each graph with the coordinates of the turning point and the points where the graph crosses the x-axis.

a) $y = x^2 + 8x - 20$

b) $y = x^2 - 5x + 6$

c) $y = -x^2 + 1$

d) $y = -x^2 - 4x - 4$

<u>Factorise</u> the quadratic first to find where the graph crosses the x-axis. Then use <u>symmetry</u> to find the x-value of the turning point.

Harder Graphs

You should know the basic shapes for quadratic, cubic, exponential and reciprocal graphs.
They might look complicated at first, but you'll soon be able to spot them a mile away.

Q1   Here are some equations. Match each equation to one of the curves below.

a) $y = 4x - 1$ **e)** $y = -x^2 - 3$ **i)** $y = -x^3 + 3$

b) $y = -x^2$ **f)** $y = 2^{-x}$ **j)** $y = x^3$

c) $y = x^2 + 2$ **g)** $y = 2x^3 - 3$ **k)** $y = 5^x - 2$

d) $y = -\dfrac{3}{x}$ **h)** $y = -\dfrac{1}{2}x^3 + 2$ **l)** $y = \dfrac{2}{x}$

i)

v)

ix)

ii)

vi)

x)

iii)

vii)

xi)

iv)

viii)

xii)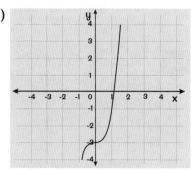

Section Three — Graphs

Harder Graphs

Q2 Complete this table of values for $y = x^3 + 4$:

x	-3	-2	-1	0	1	2	3
x^3							
+4							
y							

Draw the graph of $y = x^3 + 4$.

Q3 Complete this table of values for $y = -x^3 - 4$:

x	-3	-2	-1	0	1	2	3
$-x^3$							
-4							
y							

Draw the graph of $y = -x^3 - 4$.

Q4 Draw the graph of $y = 2x^3 + 3x - 6$ for values of x between -2 and 2.

Q5 Draw the graph of $y = x^3 + 2x^2 - 5x$ for values of x between -3 and 3.

Q6 Draw the graph of:

a) $x^2 + y^2 = 4$

b) $x^2 + y^2 = 49$

Q7 Write down the equation for each of the circle graphs below:

a)

b)

c)

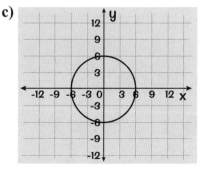

Q8 A circle has its centre at (0, 0). The point (-4, -3) lies on the circle. Find the radius and equation of the circle.

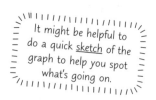
It might be helpful to do a quick <u>sketch</u> of the graph to help you spot what's going on.

Q9 A circle has its centre at (0, 0). The point (-8, 15) lies on the circle. Find the radius and equation of the circle.

Q10 Find the equation of the tangent to $x^2 + y^2 = 169$ at the point:

The tangent at a point on a circle is always perpendicular to the radius drawn from that point.

a) (5, 12)

b) (12, -5)

c) (-12, -5)

Which two of these tangents are perpendicular to one another?

Harder Graphs

These equations and shapes are a bit more alien... but just go about plotting them the same way as a cubic or quadratic and you'll be fine. Don't try to skip stages when you're working through it — <u>errors</u> will then become <u>much harder</u> to spot.

The two halves of a 1/x graph <u>never touch</u> and are <u>symmetrical</u> around y = x and y = -x.

Q11 Complete this table of values for the graph $y = 1/x$.

a) Draw axes with x from -4 to 4 and y from -1 to 1.

x	-4	-3	-2	-1	0	1	2	3	4
y=1/x		-0.33			n/a				0.25

b) Plot these points and draw the two smooth curves that form the graph.

c) Label your graph.

The O's just there to fool you — no graph with A/x in its equation will pass through x = O.

k^x graphs are always above the x-axis and pass through the point (0, 1).

k is any positive number

Q12 a) Complete this table of values for the graph $y = 2^x$.

x	-4	-3	-2	-1	0	1	2	3	4
y=2^x				0.5	1		4		

b) Draw the graph $y = 2^x$ for x from -4 to 4.

c) Why do k^x graphs always pass through (0, 1)?

All these types of equations can be combined — see what shape of graph you get.

Q13 a) Complete this table of values for the graph $y = 3^x - 6/x$.

x	-3	-2	-1	0	1	2	3
3^x			0.33		3		
6/x						3	
y=3^x − 6/x					-3		

b) Draw the graph $y = 3^x - 6/x$ for x from -3 to 3.

Q14 Sketch the following graphs on the same set of axes. Mark on any points where the lines cross the axes.

a) $y = 3^x$ **b)** $y = 9^x$ **c)** $y = 4^{-x}$

Q15 The graph below shows how the number of grey squirrels living in a forest changes over time. The equation for this graph is $S = ab^t$ where S is the number of grey squirrels, t is the time in years and a and b are positive constants.

a) Using the graph, find the constants a and b.

b) $t = 0$ on 1st January 2012. Assuming the population of grey squirrels continues to grow in the same way, how many squirrels will there be on 1st January 2017?

Harder Graphs

<u>Remember</u> — <u>Sin</u> and <u>Cos</u> only have values between <u>−1 and 1</u> and repeat themselves every <u>360°</u>. <u>Tan</u> has values between <u>-∞ and ∞</u> and repeats itself every <u>180°</u>.

Q16

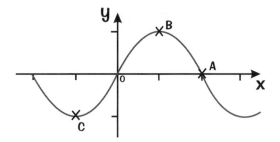

This is the graph of $y = \sin x$. Write down the coordinates of the points A, B and C.

Q17 This is the graph of $y = \cos x$. Write down the coordinates of the points D, E, F and G.

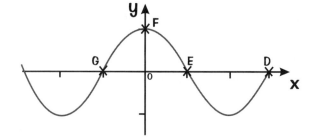

Q18 The points marked with letters all lie on either the $y = \sin x$ or the $y = \cos x$ graph. For each point, state which graph goes through it.

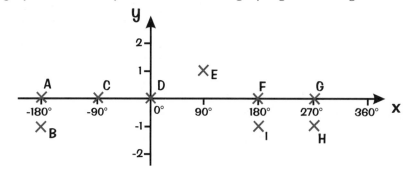

Q19 Sketch the graph of $y = \tan x$ for values of x between -180° and 450°.

Q20 Complete this table of values for $y = \cos x + 1$:

x	0°	90°	180°	270°	360°
y	2				

Solving Equations Using Graphs

Q1 Solve the following simultaneous equations by drawing graphs. Use values $0 \leqslant x \leqslant 6$

a) $y = x$
$y = 9 - 2x$

b) $y = 2x + 1$
$2y = 8 + x$

c) $y = 4 - 2x$
$x + y = 3$

d) $y = 3 - x$
$3x + y = 5$

e) $2x + y = 6$
$y = 3x + 1$

f) $y = 2x$
$y = x + 1$

g) $x + y = 5$
$2x - 1 = y$

h) $2y = 3x$
$y = x + 1$

i) $y = x - 3$
$y + x = 7$

j) $y = x + 1$
$2x + y = 10$

Use this diagram for Q2 and Q3.

Q2 Use the graphs to find the solutions to the following simultaneous equations to 1 decimal place:

a) $y = x + 2$
$y = -2x + 4$

b) $y = x^2 - x$
$y = -2x + 4$

Q3 Use the graphs to find the solutions to the following equations. Give your answers to 1 decimal place where appropriate.

a) $x^2 - x = 0$

b) $x^2 - x = x + 2$

c) $x^2 - x - 8 = 0$

 These equations look a bit nasty, but they're just made up of the equations you've got graphs for. And you know how to do the rest of it, don't you...

Q4 Complete this table for $y = -\frac{1}{2}x^2 + 5$:

X	-4	-3	-2	-1	0	1	2	3	4
$-\frac{1}{2}x^2$									
+5									
y									

Draw the graph $y = -\frac{1}{2}x^2 + 5$.

a) Use your graph to solve the following equations (to 1 d.p.):

i) $-\frac{1}{2}x^2 + 5 = 0$ **ii)** $-\frac{1}{2}x^2 + 5 = -3$ **iii)** $-\frac{1}{2}x^2 + 5 = x$

b) Find the equation of the line you could add to your graph to solve $-\frac{1}{2}x^2 - 2x + 3 = 0$.

Graph Transformations

You've got to learn the rules for these shifts and reflections — there are only 2 types of each, so it won't take long. And don't forget — y = f(x + a) shifts the graph to the <u>left</u> and y = f(x – a) shifts the graph to the <u>right</u>.

Q1 This is a graph of $y = f(x)$.

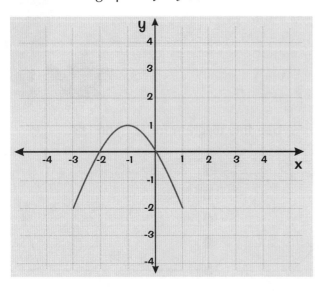

Use the graph of $y = f(x)$ to sketch:

a) $y = f(x) + 3$

b) $y = f(x) - 3$

c) $y = f(x + 2)$

d) $y = f(x - 3)$

e) $y = -f(x)$

f) $y = f(-x)$

Q2 This is a graph of $y = f(x)$.

Use the graph of $y = f(x)$ to sketch:

a) $y = f(x) + 2$

b) $y = f(x) - 2$

c) $y = f(x + 2)$

d) $y = f(x - 2)$

e) $y = -f(x) + 2$

f) $y = f(-x) - 1$

g) $y = f(x + 3) - 1$

h) $y = f(x - 1) + 3$

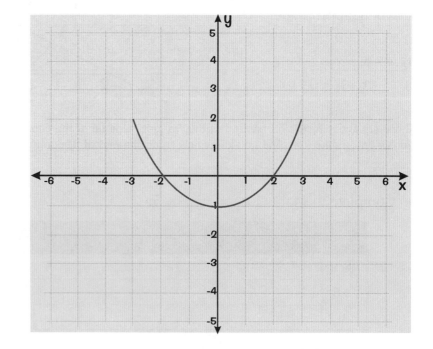

Q3 Describe how a graph of $y = f(x)$ is transformed into $y = -f(-x)$.

Section Three — Graphs

Graph Transformations

Q4 The graph of $y = \sin x$ is shown below.

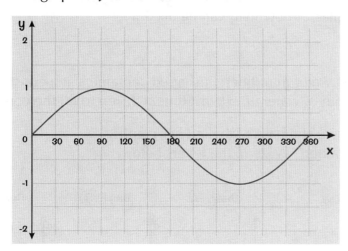

a) On a single set of axes, draw the graphs of:
   i) $y = 2 + \sin x$
   ii) $y = \sin(x + 60)$
   iii) $y = -\sin x$.

b) Write down the coordinates of the points on the graph $y = \sin x$ that are invariant under the transformation in part iii).

Q5 This is the graph of $y = \cos x$:

On a single set of axes, draw the graphs of:
a) $y = 1 + \cos x$
b) $y = \cos(x - 90)$.

Q6 The graph of $y = f(x)$ is shown on the right. Write down the coordinates of the maximum point for the following graphs:

a) $y = f(x - 3)$

b) $y = f(x) + 2$

c) $y = -f(x)$

d) $y = f(x + 1) - \dfrac{3}{2}$

e) $y = f(-x)$

f) $y = f(x - \dfrac{1}{3}) + 4$

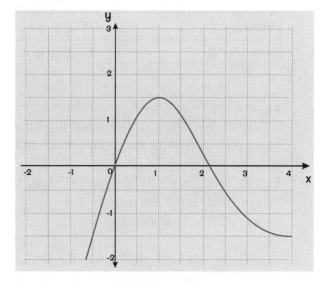

Q7 The curve $y = x^3 + 2x + 4$ is reflected in the y-axis. Write down the equation of the new curve.

Real-Life Graphs

 Graphs are pretty useful even outside of the maths classroom (no, really). Here are a couple of examples of how they can be used...

Q1 In her science lesson, Ellie pours water into different shaped containers at a constant rate, then plots graphs of the depth of water (*d*) against time (*t*) taken to fill the container.

At the end of the lesson she realises she hasn't labelled her graphs.
Which graph matches each container? Write in the letters below.

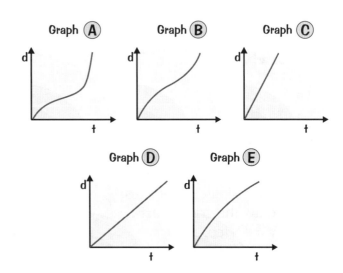

Q2 Dominic works in the finance office of a small company. He has been asked to review the company's energy costs, and is writing a report comparing two energy providers. Each provider has a fixed charge per month up to a certain number of units, and a cost per unit for each additional unit. The table below shows the rates for each provider.

	Basic price	Cost per unit for each additional unit
Provider A	£10 (up to 200 units)	£0.05 per unit
Provider B	£5 (up to 150 units)	£0.06 per unit

a) Use the data to plot graphs for each provider with 'number of units used' on the *x*-axis and 'monthly cost' on the *y*-axis. Your *x*-axis should cover the range of 0 to 500 units and both sets of data should be plotted on the same axes.

b) Use your graph to find the price each energy provider would charge for:
   i)   250 units per month
   ii) 480 units per month

c) Use the graph to determine the number of units per month the company would need to use for there to be no difference in price between the two providers.

Distance-Time Graphs

You need to remember what the different bits of a distance-time graph mean — what it looks like when stopped, changing speed and coming back to the starting point.

Q1 Dave drives a bus from Kendal to Ingleton and back again. The bus company graphed the journey to help them organise their bus schedules.

a) How long did it take to get to Ingleton?
b) How much time was spent driving to and from Ingleton excluding stops?
c) What was the average speed for the journey from Kendal to Ingleton?
d) What was Dave's fastest speed?
e) The transport manager wants to reduce the duration of the stops so that Dave can still start the journey at the same time but complete the whole route by 1630. Would this be possible?

Q2 On sports day the first three in the 1000 m race ran as shown in the graph below.

a) Which runner, A, B or C, won the race?
b) How long did the winner take?
c) Which runner kept up a steady speed?
d) What was that speed
  i) in m/min?
  ii) km/h?
e) Which runner achieved the fastest speed at any point during the race, and what was that speed?

Q3 Richard and Gabrielle are having a bicycle race. The distance-time graph for Richard is shown on the right.

a) What is Richard's average speed during the race? Give your answer to 2 decimal places.
b) Estimate Richard's speed after 60 s.
c) Gabrielle maintains a constant speed of 5 m/s throughout the race. Draw Gabrielle's distance-time graph on the same axes.
d) Who is the winner?

A curved line on a distance-time graph shows acceleration or deceleration — at the beginning Richard is speeding up and at the end he's slowing down.

Velocity-Time Graphs

Speed and velocity have slightly different meanings — but for these types of graphs they are one and the same thing, which is handy. These graphs can also tell you the distance travelled — just work out the area under the graph. Nifty.

Q1 This is a speed-time graph of a train journey.

a) What was the maximum speed?
b) How long did the train travel at a constant speed for in total?
c) What was the rate of deceleration?

> The gradient of a speed-time graph is the acceleration.

Q2 Andrew's cycle computer plots a graph of his journey but only shows his speed.

He wants to know how far he travelled.
a) Calculate the distance travelled in:
   i) the first two hours.
   ii) the last two hours.
b) Calculate the total distance travelled.

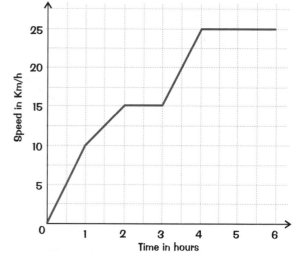

Q3 A racing driver completes one lap of a circuit.
The velocity-time graph of the lap is shown below.

To find the acceleration from a curved graph, you'll need to draw a tangent to the curve.

a) Estimate the length of the circuit.
b) Estimate the acceleration after 50 s.

Gradients of Real-Life Graphs

Q1

Fin counts the number of earwigs in a 1 m² area of his garden at the same time each day for 12 days. His results are shown in the graph opposite.

a) At what rate did the number of earwigs increase between day 1 and day 4?

b) Between which days did the number of earwigs increase at the lowest rate?

c) What was the average rate of increase in the number of earwigs between day 4 and day 12?

Q2 The graph shows how the temperature in a desert changes between 2 am and midday.

a) Estimate the rate of temperature change, in °C per hour, at 6 am.

b) What was the average rate of temperature change, in °C per hour, between 9 am and midday? Give your answer to 2 decimal places.

Q3

Sam is making a soufflé. He bakes it in the oven for 15 minutes and then takes it out and lets it cool for 10 minutes. The graph shows how the height of the soufflé changes during this time.

a) Find an estimate for the soufflé's greatest rate of growth during its time in the oven. Give your answer to 1 decimal place.

b) What was the average rate of change in the height of the soufflé during the first 3 minutes it was out of the oven?

Ratios

I don't want to spoil the surprise, but you're going to need your
calculator for this bit — get your finger on that fraction button...

Q1   For each of the following ratios, complete the statements that
describe them by filling each gap with a fraction:

a) Cats and dogs in the ratio 2:5.

    i)   There are ...... as many cats as dogs.

    ii) There are ...... times as many dogs
as cats.

b) Sprouts and peas in the ratio 3:4.

    i)   There are ...... as many sprouts as peas.

    ii) There are ...... times as many peas
as sprouts.

Q2   Write these ratios in their simplest forms:

a) 6:8

b) 5:20

c) 1.5:3

d) 2¼:4

e) 2 weeks:4 days

f) £1.26:14p

g) 3 km:100 m

h) 2.4:1.5

i) 27 mm:8.1 cm

Q3   A rectangle has sides in the ratio 1:2. Calculate the
length of the longer side if the shorter side is:

a) 3 cm   b) 5.5 cm   c) 15.2 m

Calculate the length of the shorter side if the longer side is:

d) 3 cm   e) 5.5 cm   f) 15.2 m

Q4   Divide the following amounts in the ratios given:

a) £20 in the ratio 2:3   c) 500 g in the ratio 1:2:2

b) 150 m in the ratio 8:7   d) 8 hrs in the ratio 1:2:3

> For these you add up the ratio numbers to
> find the total number of parts and <u>divide</u> by
> this. Then <u>multiply</u> by each number in the
> ratio separately to find the different amounts.

Q5   John and Peter share a bar of chocolate marked into 16 squares.
They share it in the ratio 1:3 respectively. How many squares
does each boy get?

Q6

A 2 litre bottle of cola is to be shared between three girls
in the ratio 2:3:5. How many <u>millilitres</u> will each girl get?

> <u>Watch out for your units</u> — you'll have to change them
> over for this one — and your answer should be in <u>millilitres</u>.

Q7   Oak and ash saplings are planted along a roadside in the ratio 2:3 respectively.
If there are 20 oak saplings, how many ash saplings are there?

Q8   Tony gives £100 to be shared by Jane, Holly and Rosemary in a ratio according to their
<u>age</u>. Jane is 10, Holly is 12 and Rosemary is 3 years old. How much will each child get?

Q9   Sunil and Paul work in a restaurant. As they work different hours, they split
their tips in the ratio 3:4. One night they got £28 in tips between them.
How much did each person get?

Ratios

Q10 A recipe for flapjacks is 250 g of oats, 150 g of brown sugar and 100 g of margarine. What <u>fraction of the mixture</u> is:

a) oats?

b) sugar?

Q11 The ratio of girls to boys in a school is 7 : 6. If there are 455 pupils in total, how many are

a) girls?

b) boys?

Q12 Sarah works as a waitress. Each week, she splits her wage into spending money and savings in the ratio 7 : 3.

a) One week, Sarah earns £130. How much should she put in her savings that week?

b) The next week, Sarah put £42 into her savings. How much did she earn in total that week?

Q13 An architect is drawing the plan of a house to a scale of 1 cm to 3 m.

a) Write this ratio in its simplest form.

b) How wide is a room that appears as 2 cm on the drawing?

c) The hall is 10 m long. How long will the architect need to make it on the drawing? Give your answer to the nearest 0.1 cm.

> Make sure you convert to the same units when you're working out the ratio.

Q14 Concrete is mixed using cement, sand and gravel in the ratio 1 : 3 : 6.

a) If Dave uses a 5 kg bag of cement, how much:

  i) sand does he need?

  ii) gravel does he need?

b) If Dave needs 80 kg of concrete, how much of each substance does he need?

Q15

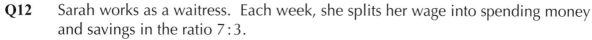

I picked some strawberries after a few wet days. Some were nibbled by snails, some were mouldy and some fine. The ratio was 2 : 3 : 10 respectively.

a) If <u>9 strawberries were mouldy</u> how many:

  i) were fine?

  ii) were not fine?

b) What fraction of the total amount were fine?

Q16 Salt & Vinegar, Cheese & Onion and Prawn Cocktail flavour snacks were sold in the school tuck shop in <u>the ratio 5 : 3 : 2</u>. If 18 bags of Prawn Cocktail were sold, how many bags:

a) of Salt & Vinegar were sold?

b) were sold altogether?

Ratios

Q17 Reduce each of the following ratios to the form 1 : n.
   a) 2 : 18   **b)** 8 : 5   **c)** 3 : 26   **d)** 12 : 25

Q18 Ben has red and green pens in his stationery cupboard.
The ratio of green pens to the total number of pens is 3 : 11.
What is the ratio of green pens to red pens?

Q19 In a box of chocolates there are 36 strawberry-flavoured chocolates,
and the ratio of orange chocolates to strawberry chocolates is 5 : 6.
If someone eats 6 of the orange chocolates, what is the new ratio of
orange to strawberry chocolates?

Q20 Dawn and Scott count the money they each have in their pocket.
Dawn has £17.50, and the ratio of Dawn's money to Scott's money is 5 : 4.
Dawn gives £4 to Scott. What is the new ratio between their amounts?

Q21 The ratio of fiction to non-fiction books in a library is 7 : 3.
60% of the fiction books are hardback, and 20% of the non-fiction books are hardback.
What percentage of all the books in the library are hardback?

> You'll need to set up simultaneous equations for the next three questions.
> If you need some more practice at simultaneous equations, see page 37.

Q22 A jacket costs £*a* and a pair of gloves costs £*b*.
One day, the price of the jacket goes up by £1 and the price of the gloves
goes down by £8. The ratio of the jacket's price to the gloves' price is then 4 : 1.
The next day, the price of the jacket goes up again by £4, and the price of
the gloves drops by a further £2. The ratio of their prices becomes 10 : 1.
How much did the jacket and gloves cost originally?

Q23 Jack's hat collection contains striped hats and spotted hats.
The ratio of spotted hats to the total number of hats is 2 : 7.
   a) Jack picks a hat to wear at random.
      What is the probability it will be a striped hat?
   b) What is the ratio of spotted hats to striped hats?
   c) Jack throws away 5 striped hats. The ratio of spotted to striped
      hats is now 1 : 2. How many spotted hats does Jack have?

Q24 Joan's fruit bowl contains only apples and bananas. If Joan randomly selects a piece
of fruit from the bowl, the probability it will be a banana is $\frac{2}{5}$. However, before she
chooses a piece of fruit, Joan throws away 3 bananas. The probability of her choosing
a banana is now $\frac{1}{4}$. How many apples and bananas were originally in the bowl?

Direct and Inverse Proportion

Remember, for direct proportion, divide for one, then times for all.
And for inverse proportion, times for one, then divide for all.

Q1   Isla is making a chocolate cake using the recipe shown on
the right. She wants to make the cake for 10 people.

Chocolate cake
(serves 6)
180 g   flour
240 g   sugar
210 g   butter
3   eggs
60 g   cocoa powder

a) How much sugar will she need?
b) How much flour will she need?
c) Isla only has 320 g of butter.
Will this be enough for her cake?

Q2   £12 is worth 33.96 Pentagonia dollars.
How much is £19 worth in Pentagonia dollars?

Q3   A recipe for a pasta sauce contains tomatoes and peppers in the ratio 5 : 2.
Sketch a graph showing the number of tomatoes against the number of peppers
in the sauce. Mark two points on the line.

Q4   Angela pays £408 for 3 months' worth of school dinners
for her 4 children. What would the cost of 5 months'
worth of school dinners be for 3 children?

Write down the number of children, the cost, and the number of months at every step.

Q5   30 bags of popcorn costs £8.40. 175 g of popcorn costs £1.96 when
bought in these bags. How much does one bag of popcorn weigh?

Q6   It takes 2 people 2 hours to wrap 60 presents.
Working at the same rate, how long (in hours and minutes) would it take:
a) 1 person to wrap 60 presents?
b) 1 person to wrap 93 presents?
c) 3 people to wrap 93 presents?

Q7   2 postal workers can deliver letters to 282 houses in 3 hours.
a) Assuming that each worker has the same delivery rate, how many postal workers
would be needed to deliver letters to 376 houses in 2 hours?
b) If some postal workers had a slower delivery rate,
how might your answer to part a) change?

Q8   Working together, Michael and Liz can paint 12 bikes in 18 hours.
Working at the same rate, how many bikes could they paint if:
a) they worked for 45 hours?
b) two of their friends helped them and they worked for 24 hours?

Section Four — Ratio, Proportion and Rates of Change

Direct and Inverse Proportion

Q9 y is directly proportional to x. If $y = 5$ when x is 25:
   a) Find an equation for y in terms of x.
   b) Use your equation from part **a)** to find y when x is 100.

Q10 $y \propto x$ and $y = 132$ when $x = 10$.
   a) Find the value of y when $x = 14$.
   b) Sketch the graph of this proportion for $x > 0$ and mark two points on the line.

Q11 $y = 3$ when $x = 8$ and y is inversely proportional to x.
   a) Find an equation for y in terms of x.
   b) Use your equation from part **a)** to find the value of y when $x = 12$.

Q12 $y \propto \dfrac{1}{x}$ and $x = 4$ when $y = 5$.
   a) Find the value of x when $y = 10$.
   b) Sketch the graph of this proportion for positive x, marking two points on the graph.

Q13 Given that $y \propto \dfrac{1}{x}$, complete this table of values.

x	1	2	3	4	5	6
y					9.6	

Put the numbers into the equation $y = k/x$ to find the value of k. Then you can find the rest of the y's.

Q14 In each of the following tables, y varies inversely as the square of x.
Complete each table, given that x is always positive.

a)

x	1	2	5	
y			4	1

b)

x	2			8
y	24	6	2⅔	

Don't forget about that little joker, the "inverse square" variation — all it means is $y \propto \dfrac{1}{x^2}$.

Q15 Two cylindrical containers are filled to the same depth with water. The first container has a radius of 16 cm and the water in it has a mass of 16 kg. If the second container has a radius of 8 cm, find the mass of the water inside it.

For a cylindrical container, the mass of water is proportional to the square of the radius.

r = 16 cm   r = 8 cm

Q16 Given that r is inversely proportional to s cubed, and $r = 2.4$ when $s = 10$, find the values of:
   a) r when $s = 5$
   b) s when $r = 300$
   c) r when $s = -4$
   d) s when $r = -0.3$

Q17 The gravitational pull of the Earth is inversely proportional to the square of the distance from the centre of the Earth. At the Earth's surface (approx. 6371 km from the centre) the gravitational pull is around 9.8 N/kg. When launching a satellite into space, the gravitational pull helps determine the orbit. What would be the gravitational pull on a satellite at a height of 100 km above the Earth's surface (to 1 d.p)?

Percentages

Finding "something %" of "something-else" is really quite simple — so you'd better be sure you know how. You also need to be able to give "something" as a percentage of "something else". Try this mix for size...

Q1 Find:

    a) 8% of £16   **b)** 85% of 740 kg   **c)** 40% of 40 minutes

Q2 87 out of 120 pupils at Backwater School have access to a computer. What percentage is this?

Q3 Donald works in South Mathrica, where the currency is the Mathrican pound (£).
He earns an annual wage of £23 500.
He doesn't pay tax on the first £6400 that he earns.
How much income tax does he pay a year if the rate of tax is:

    a) 25%   **b)** 40%?

Q4 There are approximately 6000 fish and chip shops in the UK. On average, a fish and chip shop gets about 160 visitors each day. Given that the population of the UK is roughly 60 million, approximately what percentage of the population visit a fish and chip shop each day?

Q5 At birth, Veronica was 0.3 m tall. By adulthood she had grown to 1.5 m tall. Calculate her height now as a percentage of her height at birth.

Q6 Amy has 20 pets. 60% of them are dogs and 3 of the dogs have black fur.
Without using a calculator, work out the percentage of Amy's dogs that have black fur.

Q7 At a film festival there are 40 movie stars. Daniel meets 85% of the movie stars, as well as 16 other people. What percentage of the people that Daniel met were <u>not</u> movie stars?

These questions are simple too — you just need to "find the new amount after a % increase or decrease". Once you've worked out the multiplier for the percentage change, just multiply the original value by it and there's your answer.

Q8 John bought a new TV. The tag in the shop said it cost £299 + VAT.
If VAT is charged at 20%, how much did he pay?

Q9 Four friends stay at the Pickled Parrot Hotel for a night and each have an evening meal. Bed and Breakfast costs £37 per person and the evening meal costs £15 per person. How much is the total cost, if a service charge is added at 17½%?

Q10 The owners of a museum are expecting a 14% increase in visitors next year.
This year they had 20 400 visitors.
How many visitors should they expect next year?
Give your answer to 3 significant figures.

Percentages

Q11 Tim is choosing between two cars to buy.
The first car is priced at £8495 and has 15% off.
The second car is priced at £8195 and has 12% off.
Which car is the cheapest? Show your working.

Q12 Tanya paid £6500 for her new car. Each year its value decreased by 8%.
How much was it worth when it was one year old?

Q13 Jeremy wanted a new coffee table for his lounge. A local furniture shop had just
what he was looking for — and for only £130.00 + delivery. Jeremy had £150 in
his bank account. If delivery was charged at 17½%, could Jeremy afford the table?

Q14 I wish to invest £5000 for three years and have decided to place my money with the
Highrise Building Society. The Silver Account pays 1.895% simple interest per annum.
The Gold Account pays 2.3% simple interest
per annum on the first £4000, but no interest on
any additional money invested in the account.

If I want to invest the entire £5000 into just one
account, how much interest would I earn if I choose:
a) the Silver account?
b) the Gold account?

Highrise Building Society

Gold Account   2.3% p.a on up to £4000

Silver Account   1.895% p.a

**Finding the percentage change is a bit trickier... but you'll be sure to get these
questions right if you find the difference in values first, then use the formula:**

$$\text{Percentage 'change'} = \frac{\text{'change'}}{\text{original}} \times 100$$

Q15 During a rainstorm, a water butt increased in weight from 10.4 kg to 13.6 kg.
What was the percentage increase (to the nearest percent)?

Q16 An electrical store reduces the price of a particular camera from £90.00 to £78.30.
What is the percentage reduction?

Q17 Desmond's GCSE maths exam is next week. As part of his revision he attempted 31
questions on his least favourite topic of percentages. He got 21 questions fully right
on the first attempt. Two days later he tried all 31 questions again and this time got
29 correct.
a) What percentage of questions did he get correct on his first attempt?
b) What percentage of questions did he get correct on his second attempt?
c) What is the percentage improvement in Desmond's results?

Q18 Emma makes wooden furniture. It costs her £10 for the materials to make
one chair and £7 a day to rent the workshop where she makes the chairs.

If Emma makes 4 chairs in 5 days and sells them for
£120 in total, what is her percentage profit?

Percentages

Q19 Rob withdraws £340 from his bank account to pay for a telescope, making his account £242 in debit. He then sells the telescope and deposits his takings back into his account, after which it is £176.20 in credit.

If there were no other transactions on Rob's account between him buying and selling the telescope, what was Rob's percentage profit on the telescope?

Finding the <u>original value</u> always looks a bit confusing at first. The bit most people get wrong is deciding whether the value given represents <u>more</u> or <u>less than 100%</u> of the original — so <u>always</u> check your answer <u>makes sense</u>.

Q20 In the new year sales Robin bought a tennis racket for £68.00. The original price had been reduced by 15%. What was the original price?

Q21 There are 360 people living in a village.
The population of the village has grown by 20% over the past year.
a) How many people lived in the village one year ago?
b) If the village continues to grow at the same rate, how many whole years from today will it be before the population is more than twice its current size?

Q22 A shop sells pairs of socks for £3.70 and makes a 48% profit.
a) What is the cost price of a pair of socks?
b) The shop has a sale and makes a 36% loss on the socks.
What is the price of the socks during the sale?

Some percentage questions can be a bit weird and wonderful, so you'll need to get your thinking cap on. But don't panic — as long as you remember all your percentage skills, you'll be fine.

Q23 In Melissa's kitchen cupboard, the ratio of drinks to other items in the cupboard is 3:5. $\frac{2}{5}$ of the drinks are bottles of orange squash. **Without using a calculator**, calculate the percentage of items in the cupboard that are bottles of orange squash.

Q24 If $L = MN$, what is the percentage increase in L if M increases by 15% and N increases by 20%?

Q25 The two shorter sides of a right-angled triangle have lengths a and b. a is increased by 33% and b is decreased by 12%. What is the percentage change in the area of the triangle?

Q26 At a running club, 30% of the members are male. 60% of the male members and 50% of the female members are training to run a marathon. **Without using a calculator**, work out what percentage of the members are training for a marathon.

Compound Growth and Decay

 This topic might sound daunting, but it all boils down to the formula, so make sure you get it learnt: $N = N_0 \times$ (percentage change multiplier)^n. N is just the final amount, N_0 is the initial amount, and n is the period of time.

Q1 A financial advisor is asked to predict the future value of his clients' investments. Calculate the amount in each of these accounts if:
a) £200 is invested for 10 years at 9% compound interest per annum
b) £500 is invested for 3 years at 7% compound interest per annum
c) £750 is invested for 30 months at 8% compound interest per annum
d) £1000 is invested for 15 months at 6.5% compound interest per annum.

Q2 A scientist is investigating a new strain of harmful bacteria. She needs to grow at least 4000 to have a big enough sample to run tests in the lab. The bacteria grows at the compound rate of 12% per hour, and she starts with 200 bacteria in the sample.
a) How many will there be after 3 hours?
b) How many will there be after 1 day?
c) After how many whole hours will there be at least 4000 bacteria? (Solve this by trial and error.)

Just make sure you get the <u>increase</u> and <u>decrease</u> the right way round... basically, just check your answer sounds like you'd expect — and if it doesn't, <u>do it again</u>.

Q3 An unknown radioactive element was discovered at the site of a suspected UFO crash. It was observed every day and the mass remaining was measured. Initially there was 9 kg, but this decreased at the compound rate of 3% per day. How much radioactive element was left after:
a) 3 days
b) 6 days
c) 1 week
d) 4 weeks?
Give your answers to 3 d.p.

Q4 Money is invested on the stock market. During a recession the value of the shares falls by 2% per week. Find the value of the stock if:
a) £2000 was invested for a fortnight
b) £30 000 was invested for four weeks
c) £500 was invested for 7 weeks
d) £100 000 was invested for a year.

Q5 Mrs Smith decides to invest £7000 in a savings account. She has the choice of putting all her money into an account paying 5% compound interest per annum or she can put half of her investment into an account paying 6% compound interest per annum and the remaining half into an account paying 4% per annum.
If she left the investment alone for 3 years, which is her best option and by how much?

 I'd put my money in Victorian rolling pins, myself...

Section Four — Ratio, Proportion and Rates of Change

Compound Growth and Decay

> "Appreciate" and "depreciate" just mean "increase in value"
> and "decrease in value" — nothing more complicated than that.

Q6 A small clothing company is about to go bust as business has been slow.
When the owner started up four years ago she bought machinery costing £3500.
The depreciation on this machinery is typically 2½% per year.
How much money could the owner raise by selling this machinery now, second-hand?
Give your answer to the nearest £100.

Q7 The activity of a radio-isotope decreases at a compound rate of 9% every hour.
If the initial activity is recorded at 1100 counts per minute, what will it be after:
a) 2 hours
b) 4 hours
c) 1 day?
d) The activity of the same radio-isotope is recorded at just 66 counts per minute.
Using trial and error, estimate the length of time elapsed since the recording of
1100 counts per minute.

Q8 A used car salesman is buying stock at an auction. Before the auction,
he estimates the value of each car on offer using their original price,
their age, and a depreciation of 14% each year. This value is the
maximum amount he will bid for each car.
Calculate the maximum amount he should bid on these used cars:
a) a car which cost £13 495 two years ago
b) a car which cost £8495 six months ago
c) a car which cost £34 000 eighteen months ago

Q9 A culture of bacteria increases in number at a compound rate of 0.4% per hour.
If initially there was a culture of 5000 cells, how many cells will there be after:
a) 3 hours?
b) 8 hours 30 minutes?
c) 135 mins?
d) 2 days?

Q10 Property prices in Angletown increase at a rate of 20% per annum.
At the start 2015, the price of a house was £172 800.
a) What was the price of the house at the start of 2012?
b) Show that the price of the house at the start of each year
forms a geometric progression.

Q11 An antique vase is worth £463 today. Its value has appreciated by 16% per year since
its owner bought it 5 years ago. How much was it worth when it was bought?

Q12 The population of a country is 16 million, and the annual compound growth rate is
estimated to be 1.3%. Predict the country's population:
a) in 4 years' time
b) in 20 years' time
c) 6 years ago.

Unit Conversions

You'll need to know the metric conversions for the exam, so get learning them. You don't need to memorise the conversions involving imperial units though — you'll be given the ones you need in the exam.

METRIC	
1 cm = 10 mm	1 tonne = 1000 kg
1 m = 100 cm	1 litre = 1000 ml
1 km = 1000 m	1 litre = 1000 cm³
1 kg = 1000 g	1 cm³ = 1 ml

IMPERIAL
1 Yard = 3 feet
1 Foot = 12 Inches
1 Gallon = 8 Pints
1 Stone = 14 Pounds
1 Pound = 16 Ounces

METRIC-IMPERIAL
1 kg ≈ 2.2 pounds
1 foot ≈ 30 cm
1 gallon ≈ 4.5 litres
1 mile ≈ 1.6 km

Q1 Jeremy used a website to calculate his car's efficiency. He needed to enter the engine capacity in cubic centimetres, but only knew that it was 1.4 litres. What capacity should he have entered into the website?

'Ounces' is written as 'oz' and 'pounds' is written as 'lbs'.

Q2 Express the given quantity in the unit(s) in brackets:

a) 3.3 cm [mm]
b) 60 g [kg]
c) 4 ft [in]
d) 36 in [ft]
e) 87 in [ft and in]
f) 43 oz [lb and oz]
g) 7 g [kg]
h) 950 g [kg]
i) 6 ft [in]
j) 5 lb [oz]
k) 301 ft [yd and ft]
l) 0.6 mm [m]

Q3 Convert 147 kg into pounds.

Q4 A horse's drinking trough holds 14 gallons of water. Approximately how many litres is this?

Q5 Deborah is filling in a health questionnaire. She needs to write down her weight in kilograms. She weighs 9 stone 4 pounds. How much does Deborah weigh in kilograms?

Q6 Barbara cycled 51 km in one day while Barry cycled 30 miles. Who cycled further?

Q7 A seamstress needs to cut an 18 inch strip of finest Chinese silk.
a) Approximately how many cm is this?
b) Approximately how many mm is this?

Q8 The priceless Greek statue in my garden is 21 feet tall.
a) How many inches is this?
b) How many yards is this?
c) How many cm is this?
d) How many km is this?

Q9 At the gym Arnold can lift a barbell weighing 60 kg.
a) Approximately how many lbs is this?
b) How many ounces is this?

Sylvester can lift a barbell weighing 10 stone.
c) Who can lift the most?

Section Four — Ratio, Proportion and Rates of Change

Unit Conversions

Q10 Dick is making The World's Wobbliest Jelly. The recipe requires 5 lb of sugar.
How many 1 kg bags of sugar does Dick need to buy so that he can make the jelly?

Q11 This graph can be used to convert between pounds and euros.

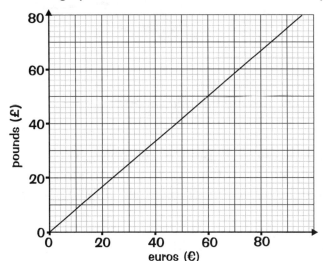

a) How many pounds are equal to €62?

b) Tim has £35. He wants to buy a computer game which costs €40. Does he have enough money to buy the game?

c) Sarah buys some steak that costs €15 per kg. How much will it cost in £ per lb?

Q12 The speed limit on a road is 40 miles per hour.
a) What is the speed limit in km/h?
b) A car is travelling along the road at 18.8 m/s. How much over or under the speed limit is this car?
c) A car is travelling along the road at 1750 cm/s. How much over or under the speed limit is this car?

Q13 Convert these area measurements:
a) 900 mm^2 to cm^2 **d)** 500 cm^2 to m^2
b) 15 m^2 to mm^2 **e)** 38 cm^2 to mm^2
c) 4 m^2 to cm^2 **f)** 860 000 mm^2 to m^2

Q14 A swimming pool has a volume of 2500 m^3.
a) Convert this volume to cm^3.
b) Convert this volume to mm^3.

Q15 A scientist measures the volume of a gorilla's skull to be 549 cm^3.
She estimates that the gorilla's brain had a volume of 682 000 mm^3.
Can she be correct?

Q16 A brick has volume 840 cm^3 and mass 2058 g. Find the density of the brick in kg/m^3.

Q17 Matt is taking part in a 10 mile race. Along the race route, there are water stops at 1 km intervals and at the finish line. Matt drinks 135 ml of water at every water stop.

The organisers of the race paid 95 pence per gallon of water.
How much did it cost for the water that Matt drank (to the nearest penny)?

Speed, Density and Pressure

Speed, density and pressure — just learn the formulas and keep an eye on the units and everything'll be fine and dandy.

Q1   An athlete can run 100 m in 11 seconds.
Calculate the athlete's speed in:
  a) m/s
  b) km/h.

Q2   A plane flies over city A at 09.55 and over city B at 10.02.
What is its average speed (in mph) if these cities are 63 miles apart?

Q3   The distance from Kendal (Oxenholme) to London (Euston) is 260 miles. The train travels at an average speed of 71 mph (including stops). Pete needs to be in London by 10.30. If he catches the 07.05 from Kendal, will he be in London on time? Show your working.

Q4   In a speed trial a sand yacht travelled a measured mile in 36.4 seconds.
  a) Calculate this speed in mph.
  b) On the return mile he took 36.16 seconds.
  Calculate the average speed over the two runs in mph.

> Remember, for the average speed, you use the total time and total distance.

Q5   A motorist drives from Manchester to London. 180 miles is on motorway where she averages 65 mph. 55 miles is on city roads where she averages 28 mph and 15 miles is on country roads where she averages 25 mph.
  a) Calculate the total time taken for the journey.
  b) Calculate the average speed for the journey.

Q6   Victor walks at an average speed of 4 km/h. He needs to walk to Askam-in-Furness, 3 km away. He needs to be there at 3.00pm. What time should he set off?

Q7   The distance between two railway stations is 145 km.
  a) How long does a train travelling at 65 km/h on average take to travel this distance?
  b) Another train travels at an average speed of 80 km/h, not including a 10 minute stop during the journey. How long does this second train take?
  c) If both arrive at 1600, what time did each leave?

Q8   Two athletes run a road race. One ran at an average speed of 16 km/h, the other at 4 m/s. Which was the fastest? How long would each take to run 10 km?

Q9   A plane leaves Amsterdam at 0715 and flies at an average speed of 650 km/h to Paris, arriving at 0800. It takes off again at 0840 and flies at the same average speed to Nice arriving at 1005.
  a) How far is it from Amsterdam to Paris?
  b) How far is it from Paris to Nice?
  c) What was the average speed for the whole journey, including the stop at Paris?

Section Four — Ratio, Proportion and Rates of Change

Speed, Density and Pressure

Q10   A runner covered the first 100 m of a 200 m race in 12.3 seconds.
   a) What was his average speed for the first 100 m?
   b) The second 100 m took 15.1 seconds. What was his average speed for the 200 m?

Q11   A military plane can achieve a speed of 1100 km/h. At this speed it
   passes over town A at 1205 and town B at 1217.
   a) How far apart are towns A and B?
   b) The plane then flies over village C which is 93 km from B.
   To the nearest minute, how long does it take from B to C?

Q12   Two cars set off on 180 mile journeys. One travels non-stop on A roads and manages
   an average speed of 42 mph. The other car uses the motorway and achieves an average
   speed of 64 mph while on the move, though the driver has to make a refreshment stop.
   If both journeys take the same time overall, for how long does the second car stop?

Q13   A stone is dropped from a cliff top. After 1 second it has fallen
   4.9 m, after 2 seconds a total of 19.6 m and after 3 seconds a
   total of 44.1 m. Calculate its average speed:
   a) in the first second;
   b) in the third second;
   c) for all 3 seconds.
   d) Change all the m/s speeds to km/h.

Q14   Three racing cars have top speeds of 236.6, 233.8 and 227.3 km/h.
   How many seconds (to the nearest 0.1 s) would each take to cover
   5 miles at these speeds? (Use 1 km = 0.621 miles.)

Q15   Find the density of each of these pieces of wood, giving your answer in g/cm³:
   a) Mass 3 g, volume 4 cm³
   b) Mass 12 kg, volume 20,000 cm³
   c) Mass 20 g, volume 25 cm³
   d) Mass 14 kg, volume 0.02 m³.

Q16   Calculate the mass of each of these objects:
   a) a small marble statue of density 2.6 g/cm³ and volume 24 cm³
   b) a plastic cube of volume 64 cm³ and density 1.5 g/cm³
   c) a gold ingot measuring 12 cm by 4 cm by 4 cm with density 19.5 g/cm³
   d) a pebble with volume 30 cm³ and density 2.5 g/cm³.

Q17   Work out the volume of each of these items:
   a) a bag of sugar of mass 1 kg and density 0.85 g/cm³
   b) a packet of margarine with density 0.9 g/cm³ and mass 250 g
   c) a box of cereal with density 0.2 g/cm³ and mass 500 g.
   d) a 50 kg sack of coal with density 1.1 g/cm³

Speed, Density and Pressure

Q18   My copper bracelet has a volume of 3.9 cm³. The density of
copper is 8.9 g/cm³. Work out the mass of my bracelet.

Q19   Ice has a density of 0.93 g/cm³. If the mass of a
block of ice is 19.5 kg, what is its volume?

Q20   Some petrol in a can has a mass of 4 kg. The density of the petrol is 0.8 g/cm³.
How many litres of petrol are in the can?

Q21   A jug holds 1.9 litres of lemonade. The mass of the lemonade is 2 kg.
Find the density of the lemonade in g/cm³.

Q22   A 1.5 kg box full of self raising flour measures 12 cm by 18 cm by 6 cm.
A 1 kg box of granary flour measures 10 cm by 14 cm by 6 cm.
 a) Find the density of each sort of flour in g/cm³.
 b) Jake needs to measure out 450 g of granary flour but his scales are broken.
Use your answer to part **a)** to work out how much flour he should measure
out in his measuring jug. Give your answer in ml.

Q23   A solid piece of aluminium cut in the shape of a square-based pyramid has
vertical height 9 cm and base edges of length 10 cm.
The mass of the pyramid is 810 g. What is the density of aluminium in g/cm³?

Q24   A solid rubber ball has a diameter of 7 cm. The density
of the rubber is 920 kg/m³. What is the mass of the
rubber ball? Give your answer in grams to 2 d.p.

> The formula for the volume
> of a sphere is: $V = \frac{4}{3}\pi r^3$

Q25   A mattress weighing 450 N sits on the floor, which is horizontal.
The side of the mattress resting on the floor measures 1.5 m by 2 m.
Work out the pressure exerted by the mattress on the floor.

Q26   When a chest of drawers of weight 680 N rests on horizontal ground, it exerts
a pressure of 850 N/m². Work out the area of the base of the chest of drawers.

Q27   A large speaker sitting on horizontal ground exerts 640 N/m² of pressure on the ground.
The side of the speaker that rests on the ground has an area of 0.7 m².
What is the weight of the speaker?

Q28   A chair with a circular base exerts a pressure of 500 N/m² onto the floor it rests on.
If the chair weighs 147 N, what is the radius of its base? Give your answer in cm to 2 d.p.

Geometry

For this page, you'll need to know the sum of the angles in a triangle, on a straight line, in a quadrilateral and around a point. You'll also need to know the properties of isosceles triangles. Good luck.

For the following diagrams, find the <u>lettered</u> angles. LM and PQ are straight lines.

None of these diagrams are drawn accurately — <u>don't</u> try to measure them.

Q1 a)   b)   c)   d)

Q2 a)   b)   c)   d)

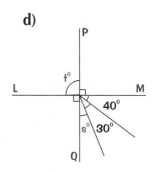

Q3 a)   b)   c)   d)

Q4 a)   b)   c)

Q5 a)   b)   c)

Parallel Lines

 This page is a bit dull — just lots of boring angles... still, that's geometry for you. Oh and by the way, you've got to work the angles out — don't try and sneakily measure them, they're probably drawn wrong anyway...

Q1 Find the sizes of the angles marked by letters in these diagrams.

a)

b)

c)

Q2 Find the sizes of the angles marked by letters in these diagrams.

a)

b)

c)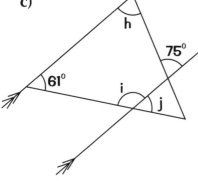

Q3 Find the sizes of the angles marked by letters in these diagrams.

a)

b)

c)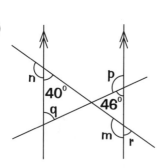

Q4 Find the value of x in each of the diagrams below.

a)

b)

c)

Polygons

Q1   What sort of triangles occur in every <u>regular polygon</u> (<u>except</u> a hexagon),
when each vertex is joined to the centre by a straight line?

Q2   Sketch a regular hexagon and draw in all its lines of symmetry.
State the order of <u>rotational</u> symmetry.

Q3   An <u>irregular pentagon</u> has interior angles of 100°, 104°, 120°.
If the other two angles are equal, what is their size?

Remember the formula for the sum of interior angles — it comes in handy here.

Q4   A square and a regular hexagon are
placed adjacent to each other.
a) What is the size of ∠PQW?
b) What is the size of ∠PRW?
c) How many sides has the regular
polygon that has ∠PQW as one of
its angles?

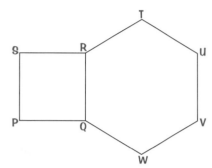

Q5 **a)** The <u>sum</u> of the <u>interior</u> angles of a <u>regular</u> 24-sided polygon is 3960°.
Use this to calculate the size of one <u>interior</u> angle.
b) From your answer to part **a)** calculate one <u>exterior</u> angle and show that the <u>sum</u> of the
exterior angles equals 360°.

Q6   ABCDEFGH is a regular octagon.
a) Copy the figure and mark on the axis of
symmetry which maps H to A.
b) Calculate the size of angle EFC.

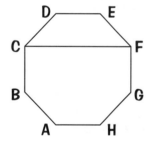

Q7   The sum of the interior angles of a regular polygon is 2520°.
How many sides does this regular polygon have?

Q8   Look at the irregular polygon on the right.
For any n-sided polygon, the sum of its
interior angles is **(n – 2) × 180°**.

a) Find the sum of the interior angles.

b) Find the value of x.

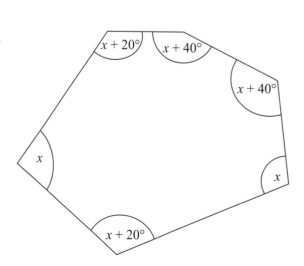

Triangles and Quadrilaterals

Make sure you know the names and properties of all the triangles and quadrilaterals. By 'properties', I mean things like the number of equal sides and angles, lines of symmetry, right angles, parallel sides etc. And by 'names' I mean 'rhombus', not 'Fred'.

Q1 Identify each of the triangles or quadrilaterals described below.

a) A three-sided shape with one line of symmetry.

b) A four-sided shape with two pairs of equal sides, one pair of equal angles and one line of symmetry.

c) A three-sided shape with one right angle.

d) A four-sided shape with two pairs of parallel sides, two lines of symmetry and no 90° internal angles.

Try sketching some of the shapes if you're getting a bit stuck.

Q2 Stephen is measuring the angles inside a parallelogram for his maths homework. To save time, he measures just one and works out what the other angles must be from this. If the angle he measures is 52°, what are the other three?

Q3 a) A quadrilateral has angles measuring 150°, 30°, 150° and 30°. Write down the names of the three different shapes it could be.

b) An isosceles triangle has an angle of 32°. What are the two different possibilities for the sizes of the other two angles in the triangle?

Q4 The shape on the right is made up of two identical squares and two identical kites. Find the sizes of the angles labelled *u* and *v*.

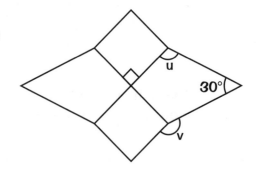

Q5 Find the value of *y* in each of the diagrams below.

a)

b)

Circle Geometry

You'll need to know all the circle theorems to answer the questions on the
next two pages — if you're not sure about them, brush up on them now.

Q1 ABCD is a cyclic quadrilateral with angle BCD = 100°.
EF is a tangent to the circle, touching it at A.
Angle DAF = 30°.
Write down the size of angle:
- **a)** BAD
- **b)** EAB.

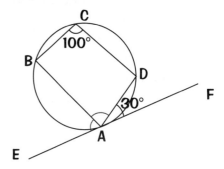

Q2 A, B and C are points on the circumference of a circle with
centre O. BD and CD are tangents of the circle.
- **a)** State the length BD.
- **b)** Calculate the angle COD.
- **c)** State the angle COB.
- **d)** Find the angle CAB.

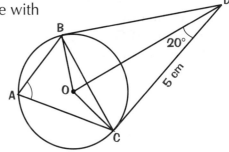

Q3 A, B, C, D and E are points on the circumference of
a circle with centre O. Angle BDE = 53°. The line
FG is a tangent to the circle, touching it at A.
Angle EAF = 32°. Find:
- **a)** angle BOE
- **b)** angle ACE.

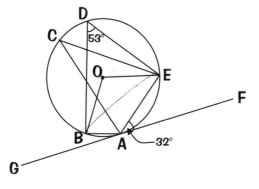

Q4 ABCD is a cyclic quadrilateral and the tangent
to the circle at A makes an angle of 70° with the
side AD. Angle BCA = 30°. Write down, giving
a reason, the size of:
- **a)** angle ACD
- **b)** angle BAD.

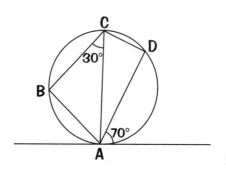

Q5

A, B, C and D are points on the circumference of a circle.
Angle ABD = $(3x + 40)°$ and angle ACD = $(6x - 50)°$.
- **a)** Give a reason why angle ABD and angle ACD are the same.
- **b)** Form an equation in x and, by solving it, find the size of angle ABD.

Section Five — Geometry and Measures

Circle Geometry

Q6   O is the centre of a circle, AB is a tangent
to the circle and CE is a chord.
Find the size of:
a) angle CEO
b) angle EDO
c) angle COD.

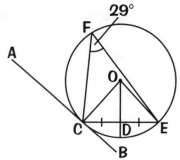

Q7   A, B, C and D are points on the circumference
of a circle. O is the centre of the circle,
AC is a diameter and angle AOD = 140°.
Write down:
a) angle ABD
b) angle ABC
c) angle DBC.

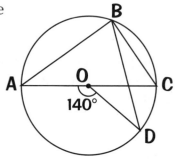

Q8   A tangent of a circle is drawn, touching it at A.
C and B are two other points on the circumference
and AOB is a diameter. O is the centre of the circle.
Angle ABC is 23°.
a) Write down the size of angle ACB, giving a reason
for your answer.
b) Find the size of the angle marked $x°$ in the diagram.

Q9

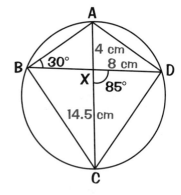

ABCD is a cyclic quadrilateral. The lines AC and BD
intersect at X. Lengths AX = 4 cm, DX = 8 cm and
XC = 14.5 cm. Angle DXC = 85° and ABD = 30°.
a) Show that triangles DXC and AXB are similar.
b) Find the length of XB.
c) Write down the size of angle BDC.

Q10   ABCD is a cyclic quadrilateral.
X is a point inside the circle.
Angle ADC = 92° and angle AXC = 178°.
Show that point X is NOT the centre of the circle.

> Think about the properties of cyclic
> quadrilaterals and angles at the
> centre/circumference of a circle.

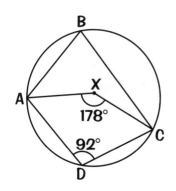

Congruent Shapes

...nditions you need to prove that triangles are congruent —
...IS (you only need to show that one of these is true, not all four).

...e congruent? Explain why.

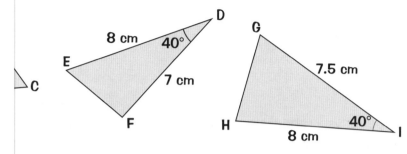

...ruent to the triangle shown on the
...ith vertices at three of the dots.
...ferent ways this can be done.

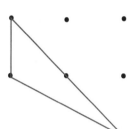

...m. M is the point
where the diagonals AC and BD intersect.
Prove that the triangles ABM and CDM
are congruent.

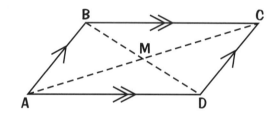

Q4   The circle on the right has centre O. AB is a chord.
Prove that triangles AOC and BOC are congruent.

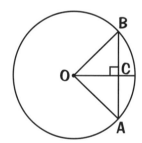

Q5   The lengths AB and BC of the triangle on the right are equal.
By bisecting the angle ABC, use the congruence conditions to
prove that the base angles in any isosceles triangle are equal.

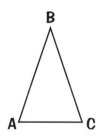

Q6   The lines AEC and DEB in the diagram on the right are straight
lines. Prove that the triangles ABE and DEC are congruent.

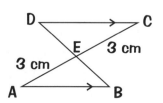

Similar Shapes

Similar shapes are exactly the same shape, but can be different sizes. Watch out for shapes being rotated or reflected — this doesn't stop them being similar.

Q1 Show that triangles ACE and BCD are similar.

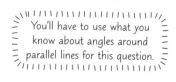
You'll have to use what you know about angles around parallel lines for this question.

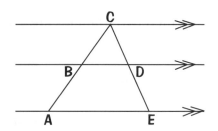

Q2 Jasper buys a model statue of a man from a museum gift shop. The real statue is standing on a plinth. He places the model on a table in front of the real statue so the feet of the statues are the same height above the ground.

When Jasper is 1 m away from the model and looks at it with his eyes at the same level as the feet, the model appears to exactly cover the real statue, which is 5 m away. The model is 30 cm tall. How tall is the real statue?

Q3 In the diagram below, BC is parallel to DE.
AB = 12 cm, BD = 8 cm, DE = 25 cm and CE = 10 cm.

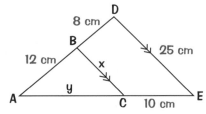

a) Explain why triangles ABC and ADE are similar.
b) Find the lengths of x and y in the diagram.

Q4 A boy made a symmetrical framework with metal rods as shown. Lengths AB = BC, ST = TC and AP = PQ. Angle BVC = 90° and length BV = 9 cm.

a) Find two triangles which are similar to triangle ABC.
b) Calculate the length of AP.
   Hence write down the length of PT.
c) Calculate the area of triangle ABC.
d) Find the area of triangle APQ.
   Give your answer correct to 3 significant figures.
e) Hence write down the area of PQBST correct to 2 significant figures.

Q5 A cylindrical bottle can hold 1 litre of oil. A second cylindrical bottle has twice the radius but the same height. It also contains oil.
a) Explain why these bottles are not similar.
b) How much oil can the larger bottle hold?

The Four Transformations

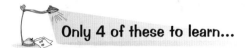

Only 4 of these to learn...

Q1 Copy the axes and mark on triangle A
with corners (-1, 2), (0, 4) and (-2, 4).
Use a scale of 1 cm to 1 unit.

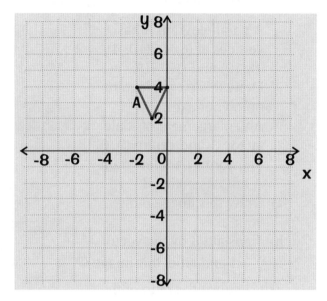

a) Reflect A in the line $y = -x$.
Label this image B.
b) Reflect A in the line $x = 1$.
Label the image C.
c) Reflect A in the line $y = -1$.
Label the image D.
d) Translate triangle D with the vector $\binom{4}{2}$.
Label this image E.
e) Translate triangle C with the vector $\binom{3}{-3}$.
Label this image F.
f) Enlarge A by a scale factor of 3,
centre (0, 4). Label this image G.
g) Describe fully the rotation that sends C to E.

It helps to label the corners of
the triangle so you can see
exactly what goes where when
you do the transformations.

Q2 Copy the axes using a scale of 1 cm to
1 unit. Mark on the axes a quadrilateral
Q with corners (-2, 1), (-3, 1), (-3, 3)
and (-2, 3).

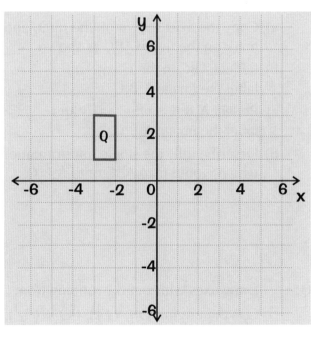

a) Rotate Q clockwise through 90°
about the point (-1, 2). Label the
image R.
b) Rotate R clockwise through 90°
about the point (0, 1). Label the
image S.
c) Describe fully the rotation that
maps Q to S.
d) Rotate Q through 180° about the
point (-½, -1). Label the image T.
e) Rotate Q anticlockwise through 90°
about the point (-1, -1). Label the
image U.
f) Enlarge Q by a scale factor of -2,
centre (0, 0). Label this image V.
g) Describe fully the rotation that sends U to T.

The Four Transformations

Move each point separately — then check your shape hasn't done anything unexpected while you weren't looking.

Q3 Copy the axes below using a scale of 1 cm to 1 unit.

A parallelogram A has vertices at (6, 4), (10, 4), (8, 10) and (12, 10). Draw this parallelogram onto your axes.
An enlargement of scale factor ½ and centre (0, 0) transforms parallelogram A onto its image B.

a) Draw this image B on your axes.

b) Translate B by the vector $\left(\begin{smallmatrix} -3 \\ -2 \end{smallmatrix}\right)$ and label this image C.

c) Calculate the ratio of the area of parallelogram C to the area of parallelogram A.

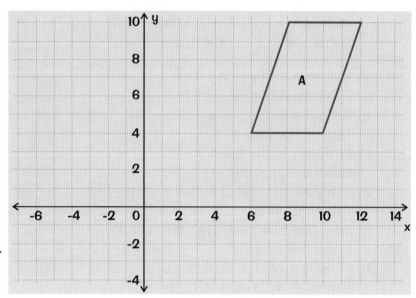

Q4 A is the point (4, 3), B is (4, 1) and C is (5, 1).

a) Copy the axes shown on the right, and mark on the figure ABC as shown.

b) Reflect ABC in the x-axis and label the image $A_1B_1C_1$.

c) Reflect $A_1B_1C_1$ in the y-axis and label the image $A_2B_2C_2$.

d) Describe fully the single transformation which would map ABC onto $A_2B_2C_2$.

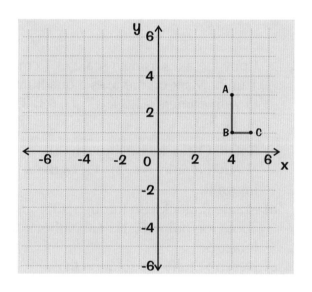

Q5 Draw axes with x and y running from 0 to 12 with a scale of 1 cm to 1 unit.
O is the origin. $\overrightarrow{OP} = \left(\begin{smallmatrix} 4 \\ 2 \end{smallmatrix}\right)$, $\overrightarrow{PQ} = \left(\begin{smallmatrix} -1 \\ 2 \end{smallmatrix}\right)$, and $\overrightarrow{QR} = 2\overrightarrow{OP}$.

a) Mark P, Q and R on your axes.

b) Translate R by $\overrightarrow{QO}$. Label the image T.

c) Verify that $\overrightarrow{PQ} + \overrightarrow{QR} + \overrightarrow{RT} + \overrightarrow{TP} = \left(\begin{smallmatrix} 0 \\ 0 \end{smallmatrix}\right)$.

Urghh — vectors...
Make sure you get the coordinates the right way round — top for x direction, bottom for y direction.

Section Five — Geometry and Measures

Perimeter and Area

There are quite a few formulas you need to know for perimeter and area questions.
Most of them are dead easy though — but watch out for tricky contexts.

Q1 A rectangular dining room, with a width equal to half its length, needs carpet tiling.
    a) Calculate the area of the floor, if its width is 12 m.
    b) If carpet tiles are 50 cm by 50 cm squares, calculate how many tiles will be required.
    c) If carpet tiles cost £4.99 per m², calculate the <u>cost</u> of tiling the dining room.

Q2 Natasha is training for a marathon by jogging around the outside of a square
field of area 9000 m². One evening, Natasha completed 11 laps of the field.
How far did she run? Give your answer to the nearest 100 m.

Q3 A rectangular lawn with an area of 48 m² is being made.
If its width is 5 m, how long is it?
How many rolls of turf 50 cm wide and 11 m long should be ordered to grass this area?

Q4 This parallelogram has an area of 4773 mm².
How long is its base?

Q5 Josh is making a cube bean bag out of material for his textiles coursework.
If each side of the cube is to have edges of length 60 cm,
how many <u>square metres</u> of material will Josh need?

Q6 A fighter aircraft's wing is shown on the right.
Calculate its area and its perimeter.

Two lots of Pythagoras are needed
to find the length of the third side.

Q7 Jon is making a metal bracket as part of his technology project.
The bracket is stamped out of sheet metal in a 2 phase process:
1st: The <u>outer triangle</u>, measuring 14.4 cm by 10 cm,
is stamped out.
2nd: A smaller <u>inner triangle</u> measuring 5.76 cm by 4 cm
is stamped out of the larger triangle.
The bracket should be made from no more than 50 cm²
of sheet metal if the fixing is to support its weight.
Will the fixing take the weight of Jon's bracket?

Perimeter and Area

Q8 Calculate the area of a rhombus with diagonals 7 km and 11 km.

> You'll need to split the rhombus into triangles for this question.

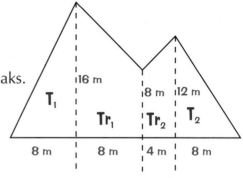

Q9 A modern glass sculpture is to be erected. It is made from glass in the shape of two mountain peaks. Calculate each _separate_ area and hence find the _total_ area of glass required.

Q10 A simple tent is to be made in the shape of a triangular prism. The dimensions are shown in the diagram.

a) The two end faces are isosceles triangles. Find their areas.

b) The two sides and ground sheet are rectangles. Find their areas.

c) How much material is required to make this tent?

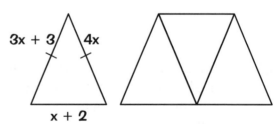

Q11 A square with side length x cm is cut in half vertically, and the two pieces are joined together to make a rectangle (as shown in the diagram below).

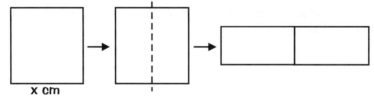

x cm

In terms of x, find an expression for:

a) the perimeter of the rectangle,

b) the area of the rectangle.

Q12 The diagram on the right shows the dimensions, given in cm, of an isosceles triangle. The diagram also shows a trapezium made up of three isosceles triangles, each identical to the one given. Find the perimeter of the trapezium.

$3x + 3$ / \ $4x$

$x + 2$

Q13 The square and the rectangle shown have the same area. The perimeter of the rectangle is 6 units bigger than the perimeter of the square. Find the values of x and y correct to 2 d.p.

x

y

$3x + 1$

Area — Circles

Another page, another load of formulas you need to know. *Sigh*. As well as area and circumference, you also need to know how to find the area of a sector and length of an arc.

Q1 A <u>minor sector</u> is labelled A on the diagram.
Name the features labelled B, C and D.

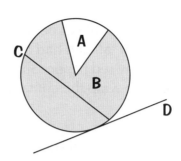

Q2 Find each of the following.
a) The area of a circle with radius = 6.12 m. Give your answer <u>to 2 dp</u>.
b) The circumference of a circle with radius = 7.2 m. Give your answer <u>to 2 sf</u>.
c) The circumference of a circle with diameter = 14.8 m. Give your answer <u>to 1 dp</u>.
d) The area of a circle with diameter = 4.246 cm. Give your answer <u>to 3 sf</u>.

Q3 Find the <u>area and the perimeter</u> of each of the shapes drawn here.

a)

b)

c)

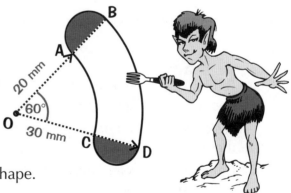

Q4 A plastic strip is made in the shape shown.
The curves AC and BD are both arcs of
circles with centre O. The larger circle has
radius 30 mm and the smaller circle has
radius 20 mm. The shaded ends of the shape
are both semicircles.

a) Find the area of the unshaded shape ABDC.
b) Find the area of the two semicircular ends.
Hence write down the area of the complete shape.
c) Find the perimeter of the complete shape.

Q5

Side View

A washing powder ball looks from the side like a
circle with the shaded area removed. The circle
has radius 5 cm and the angle AOB = 80°.
a) Find the area of the sector OAB.
b) Find the area of triangle AOB
and hence the shaded area.

The formula you need for part b) is area = ½ ab sin C.

3D Shapes — Surface Area

If you're struggling with surface area, it might help to sketch the net of the shape — that's what you'd get if you unfolded a 3D shape and laid it out flat. The area of the net is the same as the surface area.

Q1 Hannah bought a bottle of perfume as a present in a cylindrical container, which was 20 cm tall and had a radius of 4 cm. She wanted to wrap the container in shiny red paper. She has enough paper to cover an area of 600 cm². Is that enough to wrap the container?

Q2 Find the surface area of a sphere with a diameter of 6 cm.

6 cm

Q3 Which of these two shapes has the greater surface area? Show your working.

8 cm

3 cm

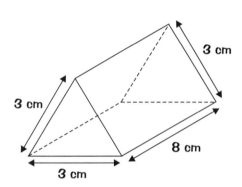

3 cm

3 cm

3 cm

8 cm

Q4 A hemisphere has a surface area of 75π cm². Find the radius, in cm, of the hemisphere.

Q5 Bill has a greenhouse with dimensions as shown. The roof is made up of eight panels of equal size.

A storm breaks all of the glass in the shaded area on the diagram.

Calculate the area of glass which Bill must buy to repair his greenhouse.

Look for a right-angled triangle to calculate AB.

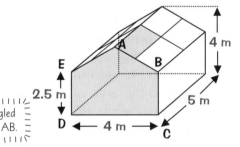

A

B

4 m

E

2.5 m

5 m

D ◄— 4 m —► C

Q6 Kaphiri is planning to build a square-based pyramid with dimensions as shown in the diagram.

a) What will the surface area of the whole pyramid be?

b) A 1 litre tin of paint will cover 15 m². Kaphiri wants to paint the four triangular faces of the pyramid. How many tins of paint will Kaphiri need?

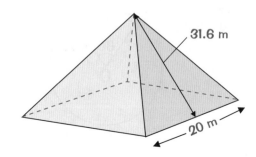

31.6 m

20 m

3D Shapes — Volume

Learn to love the <u>volume formulas</u> for <u>cuboids</u>, <u>spheres</u>, <u>prisms</u>, <u>pyramids</u> and <u>cones</u>.

> Volume of pyramid $= \frac{1}{3} \times$ base area $\times$ vertical height
> Volume of cone $= \frac{1}{3} \times \pi r^2 \times$ vertical height
> Volume of sphere $= \frac{4}{3} \times \pi r^3$

Q1   Joe buys a polythene tunnel to protect his plants from frost. It has a semicircular cross-section with a diameter of 70 cm, and a length of 3 m.

a) Find the cross-sectional area in m².
b) Hence find the volume of the tunnel.

3 m

70 cm

Q2   I am planning to build a circular pond in my garden surrounded by a ring-shaped paved area. The pond will be 50 cm deep and filled with water.

a) Calculate the approximate cost of paving the area around the pond with slabs costing £16 per m². Give your answer to the nearest £10.

b) I need to add 15 ml of liquid pond treatment for every m³ of water in the pond. Find the volume of treatment I will need to add to the pond. Give your answer to the nearest ml.

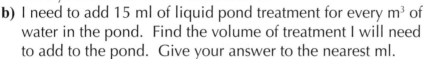

paved area

4 m

5 m

Q3   A solid metal cube, with sides of length 10 cm, is melted down and made into a solid cylinder 10 cm high.

a) What is the radius of this cylinder?
b) Find the surface area of the cylinder.

10 cm

10 cm

10 cm

10 cm

Q4   A tin mug has the dimensions shown.
a) What is the greatest volume of milk the mug can hold?
b) In fact, 600 cm³ of milk is poured in. How high will it go up the mug?

16 cm

10 cm

Q5

3 cm

3 cm   5 mm

A nut has the cross-section illustrated. The circular hole has a diameter of 1.4 cm and the nut is 5 mm thick. Find the volume of the nut in cm³.

(Units...)

Q6   Davey is pumping up a basketball. He knows the diameter of a fully-inflated basketball should be no more than 30 cm. Calculate the maximum volume of air that Davey should use to inflate his basketball.

3D Shapes — Volume

Q7 The largest Egyptian pyramid has a square base with sides of length 230 m, and is 139 m high. What is the volume of this pyramid? Give your answer to the nearest m³.

Q8 Steve has bought a pair of speaker stands. The base of each stand is a hollow prism with the dimensions shown. A hollow tube of diameter 4 cm and height 110 cm screws into the top of each base to form the stand.

Steve is filling the stands with sand to improve stability. Find the volume of sand Steve needs to use to fill both stands (the bases _and_ the tubes). Give your answer in litres to 2 d.p.

1 litre = 1000 cm³

Q9

Jill buys a bookshelf with the dimensions shown in the diagram.
a) Find the cross-sectional area.
b) Find the volume of the bookshelf in m³.

Q10 Giles is making Christmas baubles by filling plastic spheres of radius 3 cm with a glittery gel. He pours the gel into the plastic sphere at a rate of 5 ml per second. How long will it take him to fill 10 baubles? Give your answer in minutes and seconds to the nearest second.

Q11 An egg timer is symmetrical and consists of hemispheres, cylinders and cones joined together as shown to the left.

a) Calculate the volume of sand in the upper container.

You need to find three volumes and add them together.

Sand runs into the bottom container at a constant rate of 0.05 cm³ per second. At the end of a certain time period the sand has fallen through into the bottom container as shown to the right.

b) How high (_h_) has it risen up the cylindrical part of the bottom container?

c) How long has it taken the sand to fall through until it is at this height?

2.6 cm

1.8 cm

1.2 cm

0.3 cm

1.2 cm

_h_

3D Shapes — Volume

Q12

chocolate

An ice-cream cone is 10 cm deep and has a base diameter of 5 cm.
The bottom 4 cm of the cone is filled with solid chocolate as shown.
The rest of the cone is filled with ice cream and a hemisphere of
ice cream is mounted on top so that the base of the hemisphere
coincides with the base of the cone.

a) Calculate the volume of ice cream required to make one ice cream.
b) Calculate the outer surface area of the cone.

Q13

Mike and Shelly are doing an experiment to find the radius of a
marble. They fill a cylindrical container of diameter 10 cm and
height 20 cm with water to a depth of 10 cm. 200 identical marbles
are now submerged in the water. The depth increases to 14.5 cm.
Calculate the radius of one marble.

The volume increase is a cylinder and you're told the height.

Q14 A cuboid has a height of x m, a width of $(3 - x)$ m and a length of $(5 - x)$ m.

a) Write down an expression for the volume
of the cuboid.
b) Complete the table of values using your
expression for the volume of the cuboid.
c) Draw a graph of V against x for $0 \leqslant x \leqslant 3$.
d) Use your graph to estimate the maximum volume
of the cuboid.
e) Estimate the surface area of the cuboid when the
volume is at its maximum.
f) A particular cuboid has a volume of 6 m³.
By using your graph to find the two possible values
of x, estimate the maximum total surface area of
the cuboid for this volume.

x	0	1	2	3
V			6	

Q15 A pipe has a hexagonal cross-section with dimensions as shown.
Water comes halfway up the pipe and is 4 cm deep.
a) Find the cross-sectional area of water in the pipe.

The water is flowing at a rate of 500 cm³ per minute.
b) Find the speed of the water in cm/s to 3 s.f.

*Convert the rate of flow into cm³/s, then
find the speed by dividing the rate of flow
by the cross-sectional area from part a).*

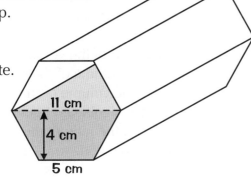

Section Five — Geometry and Measures

More Enlargements

Don't forget that when you're enlarging areas and volumes,
there's a bigger scale factor — that one catches everyone out.

Q1 For a graphics project, Eliza makes a model of a
chocolate box in the shape of a cuboid 5 cm long,
2 cm wide and 3 cm high.

a) Calculate the area of material needed to make the model
(assuming no flaps are required for gluing).

b) Eliza decides that the full size packaging will be similar to
the model, but with lengths enlarged by a scale factor of 4.
Calculate the area of material Eliza needs to make a full-size box.

Q2 Sharon has a fish tank which is 42 cm wide and has a
volume of 30 litres. She sees an enlarged version of
this in the pet shop which is 63 cm wide. What is the
volume of the larger fish tank to the nearest litre?

Q3 Soup comes in two different-sized tins — large and small. The tins are similar cylinders.
The volume of the large tin is 1200 cm³ and the volume of the small tin is 150 cm³.
The surface area of the large tin is 600 cm². Find the surface area of the small tin.

Q4 Cuboid A and cuboid B are similar. The surface area of cuboid A is 38 cm²,
and the surface area of cuboid B is 237.5 cm².

a) The height of cuboid A is 4 cm. What is the height of cuboid B?

b) What is the volume of cuboid A as a percentage of the volume of cuboid B?

Q5 On a holiday near the sea, children built a sandcastle in the shape of a cone.
The radius of the base is 100 cm and the height is 100 cm.

a) What is the volume of the sandcastle in m³
correct to 3 significant figures?
The children now remove the
top portion to make a similar
cone which is only 50 cm in height.

b) State the radius of the base of this
smaller cone.

c) State the ratio of the volume of the small
cone to the volume of the original cone.

d) Calculate the volume of the small cone in m³
correct to 3 significant figures.

e) Write down the ratio of the volume of the portion left
of the original cone to the smaller cone in the form n:1.

Projections

Projections are just different views of a 3D object. The front elevation is the view from the front, the side elevation is the view from the side and the plan is the view from the top.

Q1 The diagram shows an isometric projection of a triangular prism.

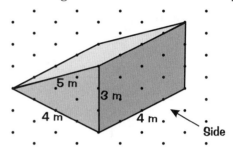

Draw:
a) the front elevation
b) the side elevation
c) the plan

Q2 Use the front, side and plan views of this object to sketch it in 3D.

Front

Side

Plan

Q3 The diagrams below show the front elevation and plan view of a house. Use these to draw the side elevation. Use a scale of 1 cm = 1 m.

Front elevation

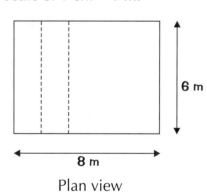

Plan view

Q4 Draw the front elevation, side elevation and plan view of the shape below.

Loci and Construction

Easy Marks

Don't let a silly word like <u>locus</u> put you off — there are <u>easy marks</u> to be had here, but you've got to do everything neatly, using a pencil, ruler and compasses.

Q1   Accurately construct an equilateral triangle with sides 4 cm.

Q2 **a)** Construct a rectangle, 6 cm by 4 cm, and label it as shown.
  b) Inside the rectangle:
  i)   draw the locus of points 5 cm from D
  ii) draw the locus of points equidistant from A and D
  iii) indicate with an X the point inside the rectangle
      which is 5 cm from D and equidistant from A and D.

Q3   Construct triangle PQR accurately with length PQ = 10.5 cm,
    angle PQR = 95° and angle RPQ = 32°.
  a) Construct the perpendicular bisector of the line PR.
      Draw in point A where the bisector crosses the line PQ.
  b) Bisect angle PRQ. Draw in point B where the bisector
      crosses the line PQ. Measure the length BA.

Q4   Omar is doing some garden landscaping.
    Because of gas and water pipes, he is not allowed
    to dig anywhere within 3 m of his house.

    Using a scale of 1 cm to 1 m, draw a diagram for
    Omar showing the walls of his house and the area
    in which he cannot dig.

Q5   Construct triangle PQR with length PQ = QR = 11.5 cm
    and angle PQR = 38°.
  a) Construct the bisectors of angles QPR and QRP.
      Mark the point O where the 2 bisectors cross.
  b) With centre O draw the circle which just touches
      the sides PQ, PR and QR of the triangle.
      What is the radius of this circle?

Q6   A and B are 2 points on a straight shore, 4 km apart with A due west of B.
  a) Describe the locus of points P such that angle APB equals 90°.
  b) Using a scale of 2 cm to 1 km draw an accurate scale diagram
      showing A, B, the shore line and the locus of P.
      An outcrop of rock is located on a bearing of 060° from A and 300° from B.
  c) Indicate the rock on your diagram. Mark the spot with an X.
  d) A ship steaming due east parallel to the shore avoids the rock by following the locus of P.
      How near does the ship come to the rock?

Think about your geometry rules.

Section Five — Geometry and Measures

Loci and Construction

Q7 A running track is designed so that each point on the track is 32.5 m from a fixed line AB which is 100 m long.

●━━━━━━━━━━━━━━━━━━━━━━━━━━━━●
A   100 m   B

a) Draw the locus of the line.
b) Calculate the distance once round the running track.

Q8 Jim is landscaping his back garden, and has drawn the plan below. Two sides of the garden are bounded by fences and the other sides are bounded by the walls of the house and garage. The garden is in the shape of a rectangle.

a) Using a scale of 1 cm to 1 m draw a plan of Jim's garden.
b) Ben, the family dog, will be tethered to the garage at B by a lead of length 6 m. Construct accurately and shade the part of the garden where Ben can go.
c) Jim wants to plant a tree in the garden. The tree must be planted more than 5 m away from the wall of the house and more than 4 m away from each fence. It must also be out of reach of Ben, and be more than 2 m away from the walls of the garage. On your plan of the garden, construct accurately and shade the region where Jim can plant his tree.

Q9 The positions of two islands A and B are found from the following information:
A is 35 km from a jetty J on a bearing 065°, B is due south of A and on a bearing of 132° from J as shown below.

a) Using a scale of 1 cm to 5 km, draw an accurate plan to show the positions of J, A and B.
b) Find from your drawing the distance in km between the islands A and B.
c) A boat leaves the jetty at 09.00 and reaches A at 11.30. What is its average speed in km/h?
d) A lightship L is 20 km from J, equidistant from A and B and on the same side of J as A and B. Mark L on the drawing.
e) Find the bearing of L from J.

Q10 The triangle ABC on the right is first rotated 90° clockwise about vertex A, then 180° clockwise about vertex C. Draw the locus of vertex B.

Bearings

Q1 Calculate the bearings required in these diagrams.

a) A from B

b) B from C

c) C from D

It's easy to get lost if you don't follow the easy rule: always measure bearings from the <u>north line</u>.

d) D from E

e) E from F
  G from F
  F from G

Q2 A coastguard spots a boat on a bearing of 040° and at a distance of 350 m. He can also see a tree due east of him. The tree is due south of the boat.

a) Draw a scale diagram and measure accurately the distances from the:
   i) boat to the tree
   ii) coastguard to the tree

b) Check by Pythagoras to see if your answers are reasonable.

The word "from" is the most important word in a bearings question, so look out for it — it tells you where to start from.

Q3 Four towns W, X, Y and Z are situated as follows:
W is 90 km north of X, Y is on a bearing of 175° and 165 km from X,
X is on a bearing of 129° and 123 km from Z.
Draw an accurate scale diagram to represent the situation.
From your drawing measure the distances:

a) WZ   **b)** WY   **c)** ZY.
Measure the bearings:
d) Y from Z   **e)** W from Z   **f)** Y from W.

Q4 A walker travels 1200 m on a bearing of 165° and then another 1500 m on a bearing of 210°. By accurate measurement, find how far she is now from her starting point. What bearing must she walk on to return to base?

Pythagoras' Theorem

Don't try and do it all in your head — you've got to label the sides or you're bound to mess it up. Go on, get your pen out...

Q1 Find the length of the hypotenuse in each of the following triangles.

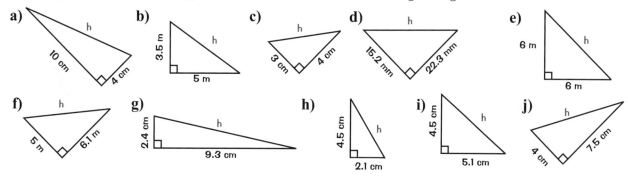

Q2 Find the unknown length in each of the following triangles.

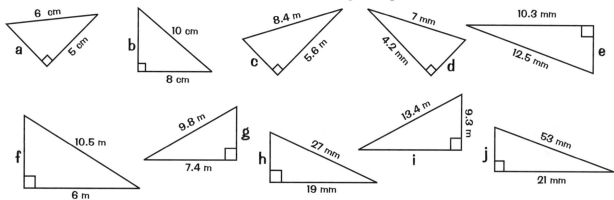

Q3 Find the unknown length in each of the following triangles.

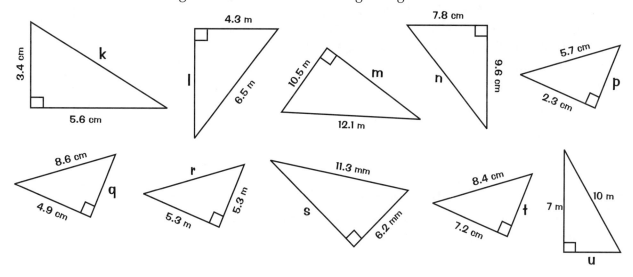

Pythagoras' Theorem

Q4 A window cleaner wants to clean the upstairs windows of an office. To meet safety regulations, her 10 m long ladder needs to be angled so that the bottom of the ladder is at least 2.6 m away from the wall. What is the maximum height that the top of the ladder can reach when used safely? Give your answer to 1 decimal place.

Q5

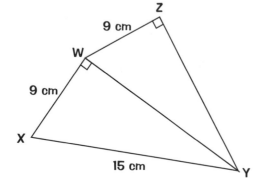

a) Calculate the lengths WY and ZY.
b) What is the perimeter of quadrilateral WXYZ?
c) What is the area of quadrilateral WXYZ?

Q6 A rectangular field is 250 m by 190 m. How far is it across diagonally?

Q7 A square tablecloth has a diagonal measurement of 130 cm. What is the length of one side?

Q8 A builder is replacing a roof beam and wants to work out how long it needs to be. It has to be the same width as the house. The measurements he already knows are shown on the diagram. How long should the beam be?

Q9 A flagpole 10 m high is supported by metal wires each 11 m long. How far from the foot of the pole must the wires be fastened to the ground if the other end is attached to the top of the pole?

Pythagoras' Theorem

Q10 Find the length of each of the lines on this graph.

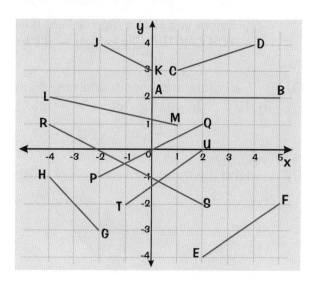

Q11 The coordinates of four points are A(2, 1), B(6, 4), C(7, 0) and D(3, –3).
 a) Calculate the distances:
   i) AB   **ii)** BC   **iii)** CD   **iv)** BD   **v)** AC
 b) What shape is ABCD?

Q12 Find the length of line MN, where M and N have coordinates:

 a) M(6, 3) N(2, 8)   **d)** M(9, 5) N(4, 8)
 b) M(1, 5) N(8, 12)   **e)** M(10, 4) N(10, 0)
 c) M(0, 1) N(7, 3)   **f)** M(12, 6) N(13, 0)

Q13 Find the length of line PQ, where P and Q have coordinates:

 a) P(2, –3) Q(3, 0)   **d)** P(–6, –1) Q(7, –9)
 b) P(1, –8) Q(4, 3)   **e)** P(12, –3) Q(–5, 5)
 c) P(0, –1) Q(2, –3)   **f)** P(–10, –2) Q(–2, –8)

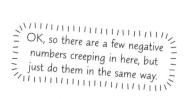

OK, so there are a few negative numbers creeping in here, but just do them in the same way.

Q14 A plane flies due east for 153 km then flies due north for 116 km.
How far is it now from where it started?

Q15 A fishing boat travels at 12 km/h for an hour due north. It then turns due west and travels at 7 km/h for an hour. How far is it from its starting point now?

Q16 The grid on the right is made up of square units. The hypotenuse of a right-angled triangle is $\sqrt{13}$ units long. Given that the lengths of the other two sides are integers, find each of these side lengths and draw the triangle on the grid.

Section Six — Pythagoras and Trigonometry

Trigonometry — Sin, Cos, Tan

Before you start a trigonometry question, write down the formulas using
SOH CAH TOA (<u>Sockatoa</u>!) — it'll help you pick the right one.

Q1 Calculate the tan, sin and cos of each of these angles:
    a) 17°   **b)** 83°   **c)** 5°   **d)** 28°   **e)** 45°

Q2 Find the unknowns in each of these triangles:

Q3 Find the value of each unknown in these triangles:

Q4 Calculate the unknowns in the following:

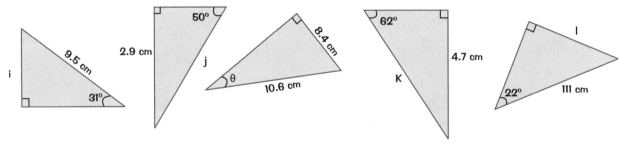

Q5 Without using a calculator, find the exact value of the letters in each of these triangles:

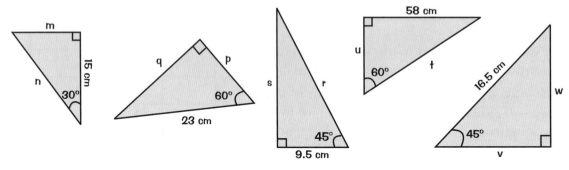

Section Six — Pythagoras and Trigonometry

Trigonometry — Sin, Cos, Tan

Q6   A right-angled triangle has sides measuring 30 m, 40 m and 50 m.
a) Draw a rough sketch of the triangle, clearly labelling the hypotenuse.
b) Calculate the size of the smallest angle.

Make sure you've got the hang of the inverse SIN, COS and TAN functions on your calc... and check it's in DEG mode or you'll get nowhere fast.

Q7   The points P(1, 2), Q(4, 2) and R(4, -3) when joined together form a right-angled triangle.
a) Draw a rough sketch of the triangle, labelling the length of each side.
b) <u>Without measuring</u>, calculate the angle RPQ.
c) Deduce angle PRQ.

Q8   The points A(1, -2), B(4, -1) and C(1, 3) are the vertices of the triangle ABC.
a) On graph paper, plot the points A, B and C.
b) By adding a suitable horizontal line, or otherwise, calculate the angle CAB.
c) Similarly calculate the angle ACB.
d) By using the fact that the interior angles of a triangle add up to 180°, work out the angle ABC.

Q9   Mary was lying on the floor looking up at the star on top of her Christmas tree. She looked up through an angle of 55° when she was 1.5 m from the base of the tree. How high was the star?

Q10   Geoff is tiling his bathroom. He needs to cut off the right-angled triangle shown so that the tiles will fit nicely on his wall. Calculate the angle, θ, he needs to cut the tile at. Give your answer to the nearest degree.

Q11   Mr Brown took his dog for a walk in the park. The dog's lead was 2 m long. The dog ran 0.7 m from the path Mr Brown was walking on, and Mr Brown dropped its lead.

What angle did the lead make with the path?

Q12   A boat travels 9 km due south and then 7 km due east. What bearing must it travel on to return directly to base?

Trigonometry — Sin, Cos, Tan

Q13 This isosceles triangle has a base of 28 cm and a top angle of 54°. Calculate:

a) the length of sides AC and BC
b) the perpendicular height to C
c) the area of the triangle.

Q14 An isosceles triangle has two equal sides of 7 cm and an angle between them of 65°. Calculate the area of the triangle.

Q15 In this parallelogram the diagonal CB is at right angles to AC. AB is 10 cm and ∠CAB is 60°.
Without using a calculator, find:
a) CB   b) BD   c) the area of the parallelogram.

Q16 This rhombus WXYZ has sides of length 15 cm and diagonal WY of 28 cm. Calculate the:

a) length of diagonal XZ
b) area of the rhombus
c) angle WY makes with WX.

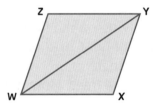

Q17 Two mountains are 1020 m and 1235 m high. A cable car connects the two peaks, with the cable at an angle of 16° to the horizontal. Calculate the horizontal distance between the two mountain peaks.

Q18 The triangles shown on the right are similar. Given that tan a = 1.2, find the value of b.

Q19 Without using a calculator, show that $\sin 60° + \cos 45° = \dfrac{\sqrt{3} + \sqrt{2}}{2}$

Q20 A ship sails on a bearing of 300° for 100 km. The captain can then see a lighthouse due south of her that she knows is due west of her starting point. Calculate how far west the lighthouse is from the ship's starting point.

The Sine and Cosine Rules

Make sure you know the Sine Rule and <u>both forms</u> of the Cosine Rule.
The one to use depends on which angles and sides you're given.

Q1   Calculate the lengths required to 3 s.f.

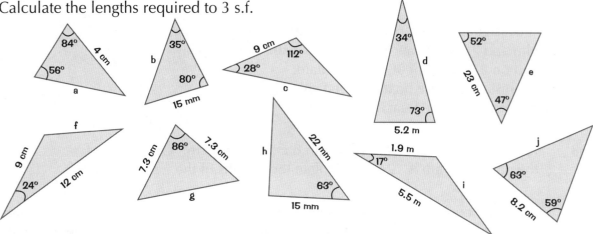

Q2   Calculate the angles required, to the nearest degree.

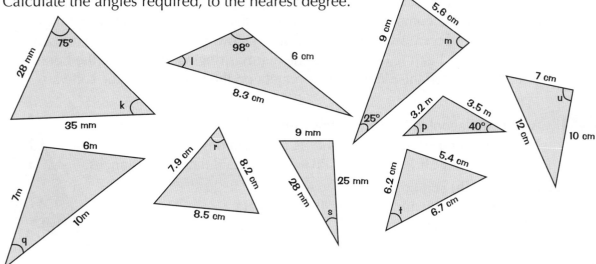

Q3   Each of the labelled angles is obtuse. Find the value of each to the nearest degree.

Q4   Calculate the lettered sides and angles.

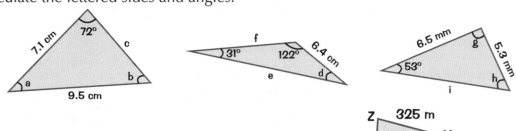

Q5   This field has measurements as shown. Calculate:
   a) ∠ZXY
   b) ∠XYZ
   c) ∠YZX.

The Sine and Cosine Rules

Q6 Peter is standing on a bridge over a river. He can see a tree on each bank, one 33 m away and the other 35 m away. If he looks through an angle of 20° going from one tree to the other, how far apart are the two trees?

Q7 A coastguard sees a boat on a bearing of 038° from him and 25 km away. He also sees a ship 42 km away and on a bearing of 080°. Calculate:
   a) the distance of the boat from the ship
   b) the bearing of the boat from the ship.

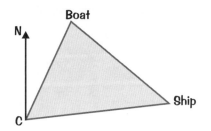

Q8 A parallelogram has sides of length 8 cm and 4.5 cm. One angle of the parallelogram is 124°. Calculate the lengths of the two diagonals.

Q9 Air traffic control are testing the reliability of their computer software by monitoring two aeroplanes and checking the computer's calculations with their own. If the horizontal distance between the planes drops to 3 miles or less, an alarm should be triggered on the computer. One of the test planes is at a distance of 5 miles from the tower, and on a bearing of 020° from the tower. The second is at a distance of 4.6 miles on a bearing of 034° and the alarm is ringing. Calculate the horizontal distance between the planes and comment on the reliability of the software.

Q10 A vertical flagpole FP has two stay wires to the ground at A and B. They cannot be equidistant from P, as the ground is uneven. AB is 22 m, ∠PAB is 34° and ∠PBA is 50°. Calculate the distances:
   a) PA   **b)** PB.
   If A is level with P and ∠FAP is 49°, calculate:
   c) FA   **d)** PF.

Q11 An aircraft leaves A and flies 257 km to B on a bearing of 257°. It then flies on to C, 215 km away on a bearing of 163° from B. Calculate:
   a) ∠ABC   **b)** distance CA   **c)** the bearing needed to fly from A direct to C.

Q12 On my clock the hour hand is 5.5 cm, the minute hand 8 cm and the second hand 7 cm, measured from the centre. Calculate the distance between the tips of the:
   a) hour and minute hands at 10 o'clock
   b) minute and second hands 15 seconds before 20 past the hour
   c) hour and minute hands at 1020.

So the minute hand is at 19.75 minutes past the hour.

Q13 A jeweller is designing a symmetrical silver pendant with the dimensions shown in the diagram. Find the height of the pendant to the nearest millimetre.

Q14 Mary and Jane were standing one behind the other, 2.3 m apart, each holding one of the two strings of a kite flying directly in front of them. The angles each girl's string made with the horizontal were 65° and 48° respectively. Assuming the ends of both strings are held at the same height above the ground, calculate the length of each string.

Section Six — Pythagoras and Trigonometry

The Sine and Cosine Rules

Q15 Find the areas of the following triangles. Give your answers to 1 decimal place.

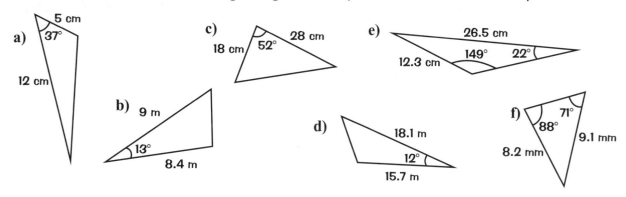

Q16 Calculate the areas of each of the triangles below, giving your answers to 1 decimal place.

You need an angle enclosed by two sides to work out the area. Hmm... looks like you'll have to use either the sine or cosine rule first for this question.

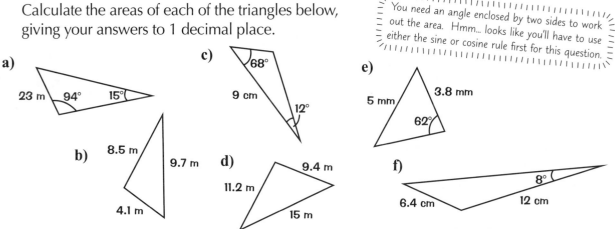

Q17 Owen's garden is split into a patio area and a grass area. On the diagram, triangle ABC represents the patio and the triangle ACD represents the grass. AB is 11 m, BC is 21 m, ∠ABC is 95° and ∠ACD is 70°. The total area ABCD of his garden is 280 m².

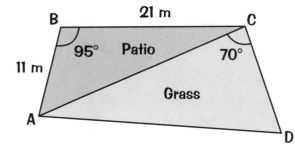

a) What is the area of the grass to 1 decimal place?

b) Owen wants to build a wall along the edge CD of his garden. How long will the wall be, correct to 1 decimal place?

Q18 Tom is painting a mural of a boat. The sails of the boat are made up of two triangles. Some of the lengths and angles of the sails are shown in the diagram.

a) What is the area of the left sail to 2 decimal places?

b) The total area of the two sails is 1.7 m². Using your answer from **a)**, calculate the value of *x* to 1 decimal place.

Section Six — Pythagoras and Trigonometry

3D Pythagoras and Trigonometry

Remember — the longest diagonal of a cuboid is found using $a^2 + b^2 + c^2 = d^2$. Always draw any triangles that you need and then label them with what you already know — that way everything's clear, so you're less likely to make mistakes.

Q1

This rectangular box is 20 cm by 12 cm by 9 cm. Calculate:
a) angle ABE
b) length AF
c) length DF
d) angle EBH.

Q2 This pyramid is on a square base with sides of length 56 cm. Its vertical height is 32 cm. Calculate the length of:
a) the line from E to the mid-point of BC
b) the sloping edge BE.

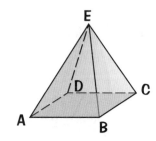

Q3 A rectangular box measures 20 cm by 30 cm by 8 cm. Calculate the lengths of:
a) the diagonal of each rectangular face
b) the diagonal through the centre of the box.

Q4

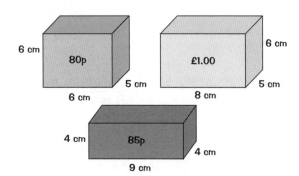

A shop sells the three different gift boxes shown on the left. Katie wants to buy the cheapest box that will fit a pen that is 10 cm long. Which box should she buy?

Q5 This cone has a perpendicular height of 9 cm. The centre of the base is O. The slant line from X makes an angle of 23° with the central axis. Calculate:
a) the radius of the base
b) the area of the base
c) the volume of the cone.

Q6 The cuboid shown is 12 cm by 5 cm by 8 cm.
a) Find the perimeter of the triangle YTW to 3 significant figures.
b) Find the angle TWY to 1 decimal place.
c) Calculate the area of the triangle YTW. Give your answer to 3 significant figures.

Vectors

Vectors are used to describe a direction with a given size. Don't forget
— a negative number means the vector is going in the opposite direction.

Q1 ABCDE is a pentagon.

$$\overrightarrow{AB} = \begin{pmatrix} 3 \\ 3 \end{pmatrix} \quad \overrightarrow{AC} = \begin{pmatrix} 2 \\ 6 \end{pmatrix} \quad \overrightarrow{AD} = \begin{pmatrix} -2 \\ 6 \end{pmatrix} \quad \overrightarrow{AE} = \begin{pmatrix} -3 \\ 2 \end{pmatrix}$$

a) Draw this pentagon accurately.
b) Write down the vectors:
   i) $\overrightarrow{DE}$ **ii)** $\overrightarrow{DC}$ **iii)** $\overrightarrow{EC}$
c) What sort of triangle is ACD?

Q2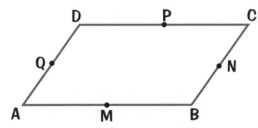

Calculate then draw:

a) $p + q$ c) $2r$ e) $2p - 2s$ g) $2r - q$ i) $p + 2s$

b) $p - q$ d) $s + p$ f) $3q + s$ h) $\frac{1}{2}q + 2r$ j) $q - 2r$

Q3

ABCD is a parallelogram. M, N, P and Q
are the mid-points of the sides, as shown.
$\overrightarrow{MQ} = x$ and $\overrightarrow{AM} = y$.

Express in terms of x and y:

a) $\overrightarrow{AB}$ c) $\overrightarrow{NB}$ e) $\overrightarrow{AC}$
b) $\overrightarrow{AQ}$ d) $\overrightarrow{BC}$ f) $\overrightarrow{BD}$

> Don't try and do this in your
> head — mark the vectors on the
> diagram and follow your arrows.
> Otherwise you'll get lost.

Q4 The grid below is made up of dots which are equally spaced horizontally and vertically.
Express the vectors l, m and n in terms of j and k.

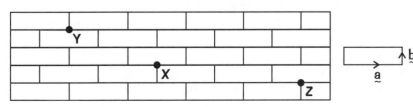

Q5 A wall is made up of identical bricks, with each successive layer shifted to the right by
the width of exactly half a brick. The vectors a and b are shown on an individual brick.

Express:

a) $\overrightarrow{XY}$ in terms of a and b
b) $\overrightarrow{XZ}$ in terms of a and b.

Vectors

Q6   In the diagram on the right, EB and AC are perpendicular.
ABCE is a parallelogram. ∠EDC is a right angle.

a) Name a vector equal to:

Equal vectors will have same size and direction.

  i) $\overrightarrow{FC}$ v) $2\overrightarrow{CD}$
  ii) $\overrightarrow{FB}$ vi) $\overrightarrow{AE} + \overrightarrow{EC}$
  iii) $\overrightarrow{BC}$ vii) $\overrightarrow{EF} - \overrightarrow{CF}$
  iv) $\overrightarrow{CE}$ viii) $\overrightarrow{ED} + \overrightarrow{DC} + \overrightarrow{CB}$

b) If AC = 16 cm and EB = 6 cm:
  i) what is the area of ABCE?
  ii) what is the area of ABCDE?

Q7   The diagram of the quadrilateral ABCD shows
that $\overrightarrow{AD} = 3\underline{a}$, $\overrightarrow{AC} = 2\underline{a} - 2\underline{b}$ and $\overrightarrow{BC} = 4\underline{a} + 2\underline{b}$.
Prove that $\overrightarrow{AB}$ and $\overrightarrow{DC}$ are parallel.

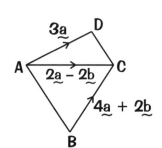

Q8   The point F lies on the straight line EG so that EF : FG = 1 : 2.
$\overrightarrow{EF} = \underline{x} + 2\underline{y}$. Find the vector $\overrightarrow{FG}$ in terms of $\underline{x}$ and $\underline{y}$.

Q9

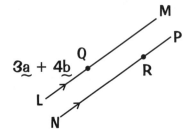

$\overrightarrow{LM}$ and $\overrightarrow{NP}$ are identical vectors. Q lies on the line
LM so that LQ : QM = 1 : 2. R lies on the line NP
so that NR : RP = 3 : 1. The vector $\overrightarrow{LQ} = 3\underline{a} + 4\underline{b}$.
Find the vector $\overrightarrow{NR}$ in terms of $\underline{a}$ and $\underline{b}$.

Q10   In the diagram to the right, HGF is a straight line where
HG : GF = 3 : 2. Find vector $\overrightarrow{EG}$ in terms of $\underline{a}$ and $\underline{b}$.

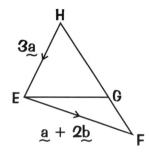

Q11   ABC is a triangle. P is the point on BA such that BA = 2PA.
Q is the point on BC such that BC = 2BQ. $\overrightarrow{BQ} = \underline{a}$ and $\overrightarrow{PA} = \underline{b}$.

a) Express in terms of $\underline{a}$ and $\underline{b}$:
  i) $\overrightarrow{BC}$
  ii) $\overrightarrow{CP}$
  iii) $\overrightarrow{PQ}$
b) Prove that $\overrightarrow{PQ}$ is parallel to $\overrightarrow{AC}$.

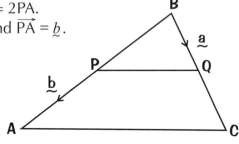

Probability Basics

Remember... you can express probabilities as a <u>fraction</u>, <u>decimal</u> or <u>percentage</u>.
1) A probability of <u>ZERO</u> means that it definitely <u>will not</u> happen.
2) A probability of <u>ONE</u> means it definitely <u>will</u> happen.

Q1   This number line is a probability scale.
Place the letters a-d on the scale to show
the probabilities of the following events.

a) The probability of getting a head on a toss of a 10p coin.
b) The probability of choosing a red ball from a bag containing 2 red balls and 1 green ball.
c) The probability of rolling a five on an ordinary dice.
d) The probability of choosing a Guatemalan stamp from a
bag containing 60 British stamps and 40 French stamps.

Q2   After 49 tosses of an unbiased coin, 24 have
been heads and 25 have been tails.
What is P(50th toss will be a head)?

1) $P(A) = 0.25$ just means "the probability of event A happening is 0.25".
2) E.g. if you roll a dice, the <u>probability of rolling a 6</u> will be written as <u>P(rolls a 6)</u>.

Q3   A bag contains 3 red balls, 4 blue balls and 5 green balls.
A ball is chosen at random from the bag. What is the probability that:
a) it is green   **c)** it is red
b) it is blue   **d)** it is <u>not</u> red?

Q4   If the probability of picking a banana from a fruit bowl is 0.27,
what is the probability of <u>not</u> picking a banana?

Q5   Students at a school conduct a survey of the
colours of parents' cars, where every parent
owns one car. The table shows the results.

Red	Blue	Yellow	White	Green	Other
40	29	13	20	16	14

a) What is the probability of a randomly chosen parent owning a red car?
b) What is the probability of a randomly chosen
parent owning a car that's <u>not</u> blue or green?

Q6   Debbie's employer organises a weekly prize draw, where the winning employee
is selected at random. Debbie only joins in if her chance of winning is at least 0.1.
If there are 8 other people playing this week, will Debbie choose to join in?

Q7   Simon has an unfair coin. He knows the probability of it landing on heads is $5 - 4y$.
Find the probability of it landing on tails.

Q8   Tamara has a bag containing n balls, each of which is either purple, white or black.
The probabilities of a randomly selected ball
being each colour are shown in the table.

Colour	Purple	White	Black
Probability	$11x$	$15x$	$24x$

a) Find the value of x.
b) Find the probability that a randomly selected ball is black.

Counting Outcomes

Counting outcomes often involves listing (in as sensible a way as possible) **everything** that could happen. Tables often turn out to be really useful.

Q1 There are 2 spinners: one with 3 sides numbered 1-3, and the other with 7 sides numbered 1-7.

a) If both are spun together, list all the possible outcomes.

b) Complete the following table showing the sum of the 2 numbers for each outcome.

In part a), show each combination of scores by writing them in brackets. E.g. (3, 7) means 3 on the 3-sided spinner and 7 on the 7-sided spinner.

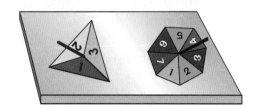

	1	2	3	4	5	6	7
1							
2							
3							

c) What is the probability that the sum is 6?

d) What is the probability that the sum is even?

e) What is the probability that the sum is greater than or equal to 8?

f) What is the probability that the sum is less than 8?

Q2 Draw a sample space diagram showing all the possible combinations of scores after throwing a standard dice and spinning this spinner. Use your diagram to answer the following.

E.g. 6, 1 means a 6 on the dice and a 1 on the spinner.

a) Find the probability of throwing a 1 on the dice _and_ spinning a 5 on the spinner.

b) Find the probability of getting a total score of 10.

c) Find the probability of getting a total score of at least 9.

Q3 A fair ten-sided dice has faces numbered 1-10. The dice is rolled five times.

a) On each roll, how many ways are there to roll a multiple of 3?

b) How many different ways are there to roll a multiple of 3 on all five rolls?

c) What is the probability of rolling a multiple of 3 on all five rolls?

Q4 A car wash offers different levels of cleaning for different parts of a car:
- 3 different levels of cleaning for the outside of a car
- 5 different levels of cleaning for the inside of a car
- 2 different levels of cleaning for the underneath of a car.

a) A customer wants the outside, inside and underneath of her car washed. How many options in total are there for her to choose from?

b) Another customer only wants two of the three parts of her car washed. Show that she can choose from 31 possible options in total.

Probability Experiments

Q1 Charlton is making a bet with his friend before the local cricket team play a match. He thinks the match will end in a draw. A local newspaper prints the team's results over their last 20 matches, as shown.

```
W W L D D W W L W L
D L L D W D W W L L
```

a) Complete the frequency table.

Outcome	Frequency
W	
D	
L	

b) Charlton reasons that since there are 3 possible results for any match, the probability that the next match will be a draw (D) is $\frac{1}{3}$. Explain why Charlton is wrong.

c) Suggest a value for the probability of a draw based on the team's past results.

d) Based on their past results, are the team most likely to win, lose, or draw?

e) Based on these results, estimate how many of the next 40 matches you'd expect the team to lose.

Q2 The notepad below shows orders for 4 different sorts of rice at a certain Indian restaurant. Use the data to answer the following questions.

a) Estimate the probability that the next order of rice is for pilau rice.

b) Estimate the probability that the next order of rice is for spicy mushroom or special fried rice.

c) Estimate the probability that the next order of rice is not for boiled rice.

boiled	20
pilau	24
spicy mushroom	10
special fried	6

d) The restaurant hosts a birthday party for 30 people. If all 30 people order rice, estimate how many you would expect to order pilau rice.

Q3 a) A biased dice is rolled 40 times. A six came up 14 times. Calculate the relative frequency that a six was rolled.

b) The same dice is rolled another 60 times. From this, a six came up 24 times. Calculate the relative frequency that a six was rolled on these 60 rolls.

c) Use the data from **a)** and **b)** to make the best estimate you can of the probability of rolling a six with the dice.

Q4 a) A 20-sided dice is rolled 150 times. A one came up 13 times. Calculate the relative frequency of rolling a one.

b) A 12-sided dice is rolled 80 times. A five came up 4 times. Calculate the relative frequency of rolling a five.

c) Two 10-sided dice were rolled together 250 times. One dice was green and the other was red.

- Three came up on the green dice 23 times.
- Ten came up on the red dice 38 times.

One of these dice is biased.

i) Explain which one you think it is and why.

ii) What could you do to be more sure of your conclusion?

Section Seven — Probability and Statistics

Probability Experiments

Q5 Kenny has written a random number generating computer program, Numbertron 5000.
He thinks a bug has made the program biased towards odd numbers.
He tests it by making it pick a number from 1 to 10. He does this 80 times.
If the program is truly random, how many times in 80 trials would you expect it to pick:

a) 4?

b) an odd number?

Here are the results of Kenny's experiment:

Number	1	2	3	4	5	6	7	8	9	10
No. of times picked	7	7	9	8	10	7	9	6	8	9

c) What is the relative frequency of Numbertron 5000 picking an odd number?

d) If the program is truly random, what would you expect to happen to the relative frequency of each number if Kenny repeated the experiment with 100 000 trials?

Q6 150 learner drivers recently took their driving test. Two-thirds of these people had taken 30 or more hours of driving lessons before their test. Among the 99 drivers that passed the test, the ratio of those who had taken 30 or more hours of lessons to those who hadn't was 10:1.

a) Use the information above to complete this frequency tree.

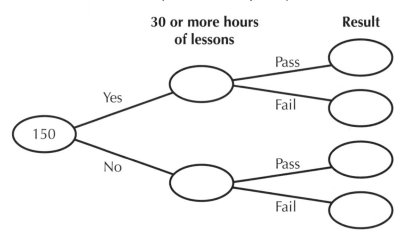

b) Given that a learner driver has had fewer than 30 hours of lessons, use the frequency tree to estimate the probability that they will pass their driving test.

c) If another 60 people who have had fewer than 30 hours of driving lessons were to take their driving test, estimate how many will pass.

Q7 Kristina and Ed each dropped a slice of buttered toast a number of times to see if it was more likely to land buttered side down. Their results are shown in the table below.

	Number of slices dropped	Number of times slice landed buttered side down
Kristina	8	6
Ed	62	28

a) Whose results are likely to give the best estimate of the probability of a slice of buttered toast landing buttered side down? Explain why.

b) Another 2 slices of buttered toast are dropped. Estimate the probability they both land buttered side down.

The AND / OR Rules

Q1 A spinner has segments that are coloured either red or blue. The probability that the spinner lands on a red segment is 0.25. The spinner is spun twice.

The two spins are <u>independent</u> — the result of the first spin doesn't affect what happens on the second spin.

a) Find the probability that the spinner lands on red twice.

b) Find the probability that the first spin lands on red and the second spin lands on blue.

Q2 A fair 20-sided dice with faces numbered 1-20 is thrown.

A <u>fair</u> dice is always <u>equally likely</u> to land on any of its faces.

a) Find the probability that it lands on an odd number.

b) Find the probability that it lands on a multiple of 5.

c) i) Explain why the probability of the dice landing on either an odd number or a multiple of 5 does not equal the sum of your answers to **a)** and **b)**.

ii) Find the probability that the dice lands on <u>either</u> an odd number <u>or</u> a multiple of 5.

d) Find the probability that the dice lands on <u>either</u> a multiple of 3 <u>or</u> an even number.

Q3 How many times must you roll an ordinary 6-sided dice for the probability of getting <u>no sixes</u> to be less than 0.5?

Q4 For the spinner shown, the probability that it lands on each of the numbers is listed in the table below.

Number	1	2	3	4	5	6
Probability	$\frac{1}{6}$	$\frac{1}{3}$	$\frac{1}{6}$	$\frac{1}{12}$	$\frac{1}{12}$	$\frac{1}{6}$

a) Find the probability of landing on an even number.

b) What is the probability of landing on white?

c) Why is the probability of landing on white or 3 not $\frac{5}{12} + \frac{1}{6}$?

Q5 Janine has an ordinary pack of playing cards.

a) Janine selects one card at random. What is the probability that Janine selects either a black Ace or black King?

b) Janine selects a card at random and returns it to the pack. She then randomly selects another card.

i) What is the probability that Janine selects a red card followed by the Ace of spades?

ii) What is the probability that Janine selects the Ace of spades followed by a red card?

iii) What is the probability that Janine selects the Ace of spades and a red card in either order?

Q6 Fatima has 16 cards, numbered 1-16. n of these cards are green, and the rest are blue. She picks out two cards, without replacing her first card.

a) Find the probability that Fatima picks out a green card, followed by a blue card.

b) Explain why the events 'getting a green card with the first pick' and 'getting a blue card with the second pick' are dependent events.

c) The probability of Fatima selecting one card of each colour in either order is 0.4. If Fatima knows that more than half the cards are green, find n.

Tree Diagrams

When you're faced with a question where more than one thing's happening, a tree diagram is amazingly useful. Practise your skills with these.

Q1 How many times must you roll an ordinary 6-sided dice for the probability of getting <u>at least one</u> multiple of 3 to be more than 0.7?

> Don't forget the "at least" trick:
> P(at least 1 multiple of three)
>   = 1 – P(no multiples of three).

Q2 An unbiased dice in the shape of a tetrahedron has faces numbered 1, 2, 3, 4. To win a game with this dice, you must throw a 4. In each game you have a maximum of 3 attempts.
a) Using a tree diagram, calculate the probability of winning a game on the second throw.
b) What is the probability of winning a game?

Q3 Fabrizio is practising taking penalties.
- The probability that he misses the goal completely is $\frac{1}{8}$.
- The probability that the goalkeeper saves the penalty is $\frac{3}{8}$.
- The probability that he scores is $\frac{1}{2}$.

Fabrizio takes two penalties.
a) Calculate the probability that Fabrizio fails to score with his two penalties.
b) Calculate the probability that he scores only one goal.
c) Calculate the probability that Fabrizio scores on neither or both of his 2 attempts.

Q4 Sam is keeping a running total of his scores on an ordinary dice using the following rules:
- If he rolls an odd number, he adds the score to the running total.
- If he rolls an even number, he divides the score by 2 and adds the result to the running total.

a) By multiplying along the thicker branches of this tree diagram, find the probability that Sam's running total after two rolls is equal to 2.

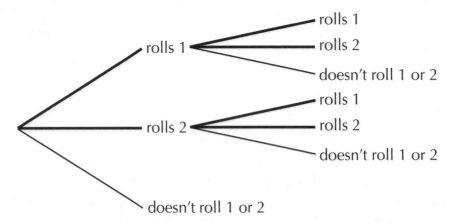

b) Use a tree diagram to find the probability that Sam's running total after <u>either</u> one <u>or</u> two rolls is equal to 3.

> Think what Sam could get on those two rolls to give a running total of 3.

Conditional Probability

Q1 3 balls are drawn at random, without replacement, from a bag containing 4 green balls and 3 red balls.

a) Complete the tree diagram below showing all the possible outcomes and their probabilities.

For AND you MULTIPLY along the branches.
For OR you ADD the end results.

b) What is the probability that exactly 2 green balls are drawn?
c) What is the probability that the last ball drawn is the same colour as the first?

Q2 Jo runs every day. Jo has discovered that if she sleeps well, the probability that she will run well the next day is 0.8. However, if Jo sleeps badly, the probability that she will run well falls to 0.1.

Jo is always twice as likely to sleep well as sleep badly (and whether Jo sleeps well on any particular night is independent of what happened the night before).

What is the probability that Jo sleeps well tonight and runs well tomorrow?

Q3 3 coins are drawn at random, without replacement, from a piggy bank containing 7 pound coins and 4 twenty-pence pieces.
a) Draw a tree diagram showing all possible outcomes and their probabilities.
b) Find the probability that the first coin selected is different in value from the third.
c) Find the probability that less than £1.50 is drawn altogether.

Q4 A box contains 6 tabby cats, 3 black cats and 4 Siamese cats. There is a hole in the box which is only big enough for one cat to walk through at a time. The cats never walk back into the box. Use a tree diagram to work out the probability that:
a) the first two cats to leave the box are both Siamese
b) if three cats leave the box at least one of them will be black
c) the first three cats to leave the box will all be of different types
d) the first three cats will be a Siamese, a tabby and a black cat in that order.

Sets and Venn Diagrams

Don't be put off by the weird symbols that go with the sets — once you've figured them out you'll find that Venn diagrams are a pretty handy tool. Remember, the squiggly symbol ξ means the 'universal set' — this contains all the elements you need to consider in a particular question.

Q1 The Venn diagram on the right shows which numbers between 1 and 10 belong to each of the sets P and Q. Use the Venn diagram to find:

a) n(P)

b) the elements of set Q′

c) n(P ∪ Q)

d) the elements of set P ∩ Q

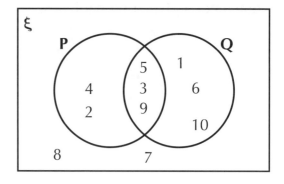

Q2 Draw a Venn diagram to show the following sets.

• ξ = {1, 2, 3, 4, 5, 6, 7, 8, 9, 10, 11, 12, 13, 14 ,15}

• M = {1, 2, 3, 5, 6, 15}

• N = {1, 2, 4, 5, 8, 10}

• P = {1, 2, 4, 7, 14}

Q3 A survey asked people if they like bananas and pies.

• 12 people said they only like bananas

• 11 people said they only like pies

• 7 people said they like both

• 3 people said they like neither

a) Draw a Venn diagram to show this data.

b) A person from the survey is chosen at random. What is the probability that the chosen person:

i) likes bananas?

ii) doesn't like pies?

Q4 ξ = {integers from 1-16 inclusive}, A = {odd numbers} and B = {multiples of 3}.

a) What are the elements of A ∩ B?

b) Draw a Venn diagram, showing the number of elements in each part of the diagram.

c) If a card from a set of cards numbered 1-16 is chosen at random, what is the probability that:

i) the number on the card is odd?

ii) the number on the card is both odd and a multiple of 3?

iii) the number on the card is not a multiple of 3?

Q5 All 100 students in a year group sat a test in English and a test in Science. Everyone passed at least one of the tests. 82 of the students passed the English test and 57 passed the Science test.

a) Show this information on a Venn diagram.

b) One student is chosen at random from the year group. Given that this student had passed the Science test, find the probability that she had also passed the English test.

Sets and Venn Diagrams

 Q6 One year, 121 films were shown at a film club.
The films were divided into three overlapping categories:
- comedies (C)
- films based on books (B)
- films that received good reviews when they were originally released (G)

The number of films in each of the categories is shown in the Venn diagram below.

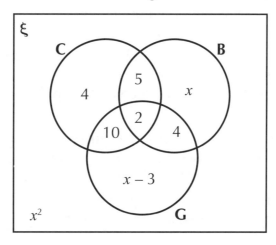

a) Find the value of x.

b) A film is selected at random. Find the probability that it received good reviews.

c) Given that a randomly chosen film is a comedy and is based on a book, find the probability that it received good reviews when it was originally released.

Q7 Alexei conducts a study into the complexity of the language used in scientific papers. He counts the words in selected parts of each paper and decides whether each word belongs to the following three sets:
- N = {nouns}
- S = {words with 3 or more syllables}
- L = {words in sentences of 10 or more words}

His results for one paper are shown in this Venn diagram. (The numbers show how many elements there are in each part of the diagram.)

Alexei summarises the complexity (c) of the language using the formula below:

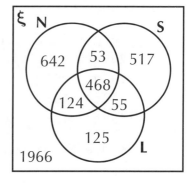

$$c = \frac{n(N \cap S \cap L)}{n(N \cap L) - n(N \cap L' \cap S') + n(N' \cap L \cap S')}$$

a) Calculate c for the paper represented in the above Venn diagram.

b) Find c for the paper described below, where the total number of words counted is 4088. Give your answer to 2 decimal places.
- $n(N \cap L \cap S) = 372$ $n(N' \cap L \cap S) = 123$ $n(N \cap L' \cap S) = 93$
  $n(N \cap L' \cap S') = 419$ $n(N' \cap L' \cap S') = 2314$
- $n(N \cap L) = 483$
- $n(S) = 1021$

Sampling and Bias

Q1   Say what the population is for each of these surveys:
- **a)** The health effects of smoking on 20- to 30-year-old women.
- **b)** The average number of trees in public parks in London.
- **c)** The average number of hours British squirrels spend juggling nuts.
- **d)** The pay of football players in the Premier League.

Q2   Professor Xavier Entric is doing a research project on
the lifespan of moorland dung beetles in the UK.

        a) What population would Professor Entric use for his research?
        b) Give one reason why Professor Entric would use a sample,
             rather than surveying the whole population.

Q3   Katie wants to know the average weekly wage earned by
teenagers in her town. She calculates the mean from the
weekly wages of three of her classmates at school.

Give two reasons why this sample may not give her a true
estimate of the average wage for teenagers in the town.

> Remember the key things
> needed for a sample to be
> <u>representative</u> of the population:
> 1) It needs to be <u>random</u>.
> 2) It needs to be <u>big enough</u>.

Q4   Give a reason why the following methods of sampling are poor.
- **a)** A survey carried out inside a newsagent's concluded that 80% of
the population buy a daily newspaper.
- **b)** A phone poll conducted at 11 am on a Sunday morning revealed
that less than 2% of the population regularly go to church.

Q5   A bakery makes 50 Battenberg cakes every day.
The quality controller tests the cakes every Friday for weight and tastiness.
She can only use a sample of 5 cakes because the cakes get eaten in the tastiness test.

- **a)** Each week the quality controller chooses the first 5 cakes off the
production line for her sample. What is wrong with this method?
- **b)** On one Friday, all the cakes are weighed, giving the following results:

201 g	203 g	206 g	194 g	203 g	194 g	208 g	194 g	203 g	184 g
206 g	197 g	196 g	206 g	189 g	198 g	204 g	196 g	199 g	204 g
205 g	201 g	211 g	222 g	204 g	194 g	203 g	198 g	199 g	194 g
212 g	195 g	206 g	202 g	198 g	206 g	201 g	205 g	201 g	194 g
198 g	197 g	204 g	203 g	201 g	205 g	202 g	199 g	195 g	198 g

Describe how you would choose a simple random sample of 5 cake weights.

Q6   Spencer wants to know how many people in his school watch Come Lancing, a televised
celebrity jousting competition. He asks 18 randomly selected students from his school
whether they watch the programme, and 6 of them say they do.
- **a)** If there are 945 students in the school, estimate how many watch the programme.
- **b)** Spencer carries out a similar survey of 18 students at a different school.
He says he'll be able to estimate more accurately the number of people in each school
who watch the programme, since he effectively now has a sample size of 36.
Explain one possible problem for Spencer if he combines the results from his
two surveys in this way.

Collecting Data

There are different types of data. There are also different ways to collect and organise data. If you collect your data sensibly, it makes analysing it so much easier.

Q1 Zac collects some data about his school. The data items are listed below.
Say whether each data item is qualitative or quantitative.

a) The colours of pants worn by the teachers.
b) The number of students late to school from each form on the first day of term.
c) The distance travelled to school by each student.
d) The star sign of each student.

Q2 Amy collects some data at her school sports day. The data items are listed below.
Say whether each data item is discrete or continuous.

a) The number of competitors in each event.
b) The finishing times of each competitor in the 100-metre sprint.
c) The total number of points scored by each form at the end of the day.
d) The distances jumped by each competitor in the long jump.

Q3 Fred asked each of his 30 classmates how long (in minutes) it took them to eat their dinner. Here are the results he recorded:

42	13	6	31	15	20	19	5	50	14
8	25	16	27	4	45	32	31	31	10
32	17	16	19	29	42	43	30	29	18

Group the data appropriately and fill in the table.

Length of time (mins)					
Number of people					

Q4 Stacey is researching the use of the school canteen.
She asks this question to a sample of students at the school:

> **How often do you use the canteen? Tick one of the boxes.**
>
> **Very often** ☐   **Quite often** ☐
>
> **Not very often** ☐   **Never** ☐

a) Give one criticism of Stacey's question.
b) Write a question that Stacey could use to find out how often students at her school use the canteen.

Q5 A drinks company is trying to profile their customers. They want to find out which age groups to target their marketing at. They use this question as part of a questionnaire:

> **How old are you?**
> ☐ Under 18 ☐ 18 to 30 ☐ 30 to 40 ☐ 40 to 60 ☐ over 60

a) Give one criticism of this question.
b) How would you improve this question?

Mean, Median, Mode and Range

When finding the <u>mode</u> and <u>median</u>, put the data in order of size
— it's much easier to find the most frequent and middle values.

The <u>mean</u> involves a bit more calculation, but hey, you're doing maths...

Q1 The local rugby team scored the following number
of tries in their first 10 matches of the season:

3	5	4	2	0	1	3	0	3	4

Find their modal number of tries.

Q2 Find the mean, median, mode and range of these numbers:

1	2	-2	0	1	8	3	-3	2	4	-2	2

Q3 An ordinary dice is rolled 6 times, landing
on a different number each time.

a) What is the mean score?

b) What is the median score?

c) What is the range of scores?

Q4 Molly is writing a letter of complaint to the bus company because she thinks her bus to
school is regularly late. Over 3 weeks, Molly kept a record of how many minutes her bus
was either early or late, and put this in her letter. (She used + for late and – for early.)

+2	–1	0	+5	–4
–7	0	–8	0	+4
–4	–3	+14	+2	0

a) Calculate the mean lateness/earliness of the bus.

b) Calculate the median.

c) What is the mode?

d) The bus company use the answers to **a)**, **b)** and **c)**
to claim they are always on time. Is this true?

Q5 The range for a certain list of numbers is 26. One of the numbers in the list is 48.

a) What is the lowest possible value a number in the list could be?

b) What is the highest possible value a number in the list could be?

Q6 The mean weight of the 11 players in a football
team was 72.5 kg. The mean weight of the 5 reserve
players was 75.6 kg. What was the mean weight of
the whole squad? (Give your answer to 3 s.f.)

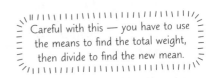

Careful with this — you have to use
the means to find the total weight,
then divide to find the new mean.

Mean, Median, Mode and Range

Q7 The mean daily weight of potatoes sold in a greengrocer's from Monday to Friday was 14 kg. The mean daily weight of potatoes sold from Monday to Saturday was 15 kg. How many kg of potatoes were sold on Saturday?

Q8 Colin's mean mark over three exams was 83%.
His mean mark for the first two exams was 76%.
What was Colin's score in the final exam?

Q9 The dual bar chart shows the amount of time Jim and Bob spend watching TV during the week.

a) Find the mean amount of time per day each spends watching TV.

b) Find the range of times for each of them.

c) Using your answers from **a)** and **b)**, comment on what you notice about the way they watch TV.

Q10 Mr Jones posted 88 Christmas cards first class on Monday.
His friends received them over the week:
- 40 on Tuesday
- 28 on Wednesday
- 9 on Thursday
- 6 on Friday
- the remainder on Saturday

To find the median, imagine writing a list of when all the letters arrived — e.g. Tuesday, Tuesday, Tuesday (40 times), Wednesday, Wednesday (28 times), and so on. What day would be in the middle of your list?

a) Find the modal number of days it took for the cards to arrive.

b) Find the median number of days it took for the cards to arrive.

c) *"The majority of first class post arrives within 2 days."*
Use the data above to say whether this statement is true or false.

Q11 Seven whole numbers have a mode of 8 and a median of 9.
Find the smallest possible range of the seven numbers.

Q12 A set of five positive whole numbers has a mean of 5, a mode of 2 and a range of 6.
Find the median of the numbers.

Frequency Tables — Finding Averages

 You've got to be able to do these questions no matter whether your table's got its headings in the top row or the left-hand column. There's no real difference — the rules are still the same.

Q1 A student has classes in Mathematics (M), English (E), French (F), Art (A) and Science (S). Her timetable is shown opposite.

Monday	S S E E A
Tuesday	E M M A A
Wednesday	S M E F F
Thursday	F E E A S
Friday	M M E S S

a) Complete the frequency table below showing a week's lessons.

Subject	Frequency
Maths	
English	
French	
Art	
Science	

b) Find the number of French lessons that the student will attend during a 12-week term.

c) What is the modal lesson?

Q2 To monitor their annual performance, a travel company logs all calls to their complaints department. The number of calls received per day over a given year are shown in this table.

a) Find the median number of calls.

b) Find the modal number of calls.

Number of calls	Number of days
10	110
11	70
12	120
13	27
14	18
15	12
16 and over	8

Q3 20 pupils are asked to estimate the length (to the nearest m) of their gardens. The results are shown in the box below.

| 10 | 8 | 6 | 4 | 10 | 8 | 0 | 14 | 12 | 8 |
| 10 | 6 | 1 | 6 | 10 | 8 | 6 | 6 | 8 | 8 |

Copy and complete this frequency table:

a) Find the mode of the data.

b) Find the median of the data.

c) State the range of the data.

Length (m)	Frequency
4 and under	
6	
8	
10	
12	
14 and over	

Frequency Tables — Finding Averages

Q4   130 students were weighed
to the nearest kg.

   a) Find the median weight.

   b) Find the modal weight.

   c) Find the range of the weights.

   d) Calculate the mean weight,
   by first completing the table.

Weight (kg)	Frequency	Weight × Frequency
51	40	
52	30	
53	45	
54	10	
55	5	

Q5   A football magazine rates teams according to how many goals they're likely
to score in a match, based on their last 20 matches. The table below shows
the number of goals scored by Spark Bridge Wanderers over this period.

No. of goals	0	1	2	3	4	5	6
Frequency	0	1	1	7	6	3	2

Find the mean, mode and median of the data.

Q6   A tornado has struck the hamlet of Moose-on-the-Wold. Many houses have had
windows broken. The frequency table below shows the devastating effects.

Number of windows broken per house	Frequency
0	5
1	3
2	4
3	11
4	13
5	7
6	2

   a) Find the modal number of broken windows.

   b) Find the median number of broken windows.

   c) Calculate the mean number of broken windows.

Q7   Using the computerised till in a shoe shop, the manager can predict what stock
to order based on the previous week's sales.
This table shows the data for <u>last week's</u> sales.
Decide whether each of the
following statements is true or false.

   a) The mode for this data is 70.

   b) The mean is greater than
   the median for this data.

   c) The mean, median and mode
   are all equal for this data.

Shoe size	Frequency
5	9
6	28
7	56
8	70
9	56
10	28
11	9

Grouped Frequency Tables

Remember... if you're given a grouped frequency table instead of the actual data values, then you have no way of knowing what the actual values were. Try not to worry too much about it... you can still do some useful maths.

Q1 The weights (in kg) of 20 newly felled trees are noted below:
272.7 333.2 251.0 246.5 328.0 310.7 259.6 200.2 312.8 344.3
226.8 362.0 329.1 348.3 256.1 232.9 309.7 398.0 284.5 327.4

a) Copy and complete this frequency table.

Weight (w, in kg)	Tally	Frequency
$200 \leq w < 250$		
$250 \leq w < 300$		
$300 \leq w < 350$		
$350 \leq w < 400$		

Use the 'Tally' column to help you count the weights.

b) What is the modal group?

c) Which class contains the median?

Q2 The speeds of 32 skiers at a certain corner of a downhill course are shown in this table.

Speed (s, in km/h)	$40 \leq s < 45$	$45 \leq s < 50$	$50 \leq s < 55$	$55 \leq s < 60$	$60 \leq s < 65$
Frequency	4	8	10	7	3
Mid-Interval					
Frequency × Mid-Interval					

a) By completing the frequency table, estimate the mean speed.

b) How many skiers were travelling at less than 55 km/h?

c) What percentage of skiers were travelling at 50 km/h or faster?

Q3 The times (n, in seconds) taken for 48 students to react to a sound in an experiment are summarised in the table below.

Time (n, in seconds)	Frequency (f)	Mid-interval value (x)	fx
$0 \leq n < 0.2$	12		
$0.2 \leq n < 0.4$	6		
$0.4 \leq n < 0.6$	12		
$0.6 \leq n < 0.8$	10		
$0.8 \leq n < 1$	8		

a) Write down the modal class(es).

b) Which group contains the median?

c) Estimate the mean value.

d) Comment on the claim that 40% of the times are less than 0.4 s.

Box Plots

Remember to put the data in <u>ascending</u> order before you work out where the quartiles come in a list.

Q1 Use the box plot below to answer the following questions.

a) What percentage of the values are greater than 20?

b) What is the range of the data represented in the box plot?

c) What's shown by the distance A? Why is this sometimes used instead of the range as a measure of how spread out the data is?

Q2 The following table shows the number of cars parked in a multi-storey car park at midday on each day in December:

690	720	580	590	210	650	640	710
700	750	790	220	790	840	830	820
900	880	480	1000	990	1020	1010	1000
80	240	370	510	460	600	580	

a) What is the range?

b) What is the lower quartile, Q_1?

c) What is the median?

d) What is the upper quartile, Q_3?

e) Use your results to draw a box plot for the data.

> Remember... quartiles divide the data into 4 equal groups.

Q3 The masses (in g) of 27 eggs are:

60	72	58	60	68	69	59	72	54	56	65	68	63	70
67	64	63	69	62	63	67	59	72	61	66	65	67	

a) Find the median mass.

b) Find the upper and lower quartiles for the data.

c) Use your results to draw a box plot for the data.

Q4 The latest census results from the country of Polygonia showed the following:
- Exactly half the population is over 42 years of age.
- 25% of the population is over 67 years of age.
- The range of people's ages is 97 years.
- The interquartile range of people's ages is 33 years.

a) Represent the above facts on a box plot.

b) Can you use the above facts to find out the size of the population of Polygonia? Explain your answer.

Box Plots

Q5 The box plots below represent the number of people per day going on four different rides at a children's theme park one summer.

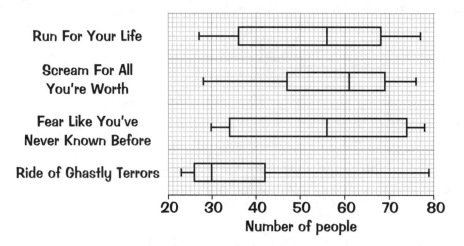

a) Which two rides had, on average, the same number of people riding on them each day?

b) Describe one difference and one similarity between the distributions for *Scream For All You're Worth* and *Fear Like You've Never Known Before*.

c) Which was the <u>least</u> popular ride? Explain your answer.

d) Which was the <u>most</u> popular ride? Explain your answer.

Don't be fooled by outliers — look for a consistently high or low number of people for c) and d).

Q6 15 students awarded marks to the following two acts in a talent contest:
- a singer
- an impressionist

The marks are shown on this scatter graph.

a) For the singer's marks, find:
- the minimum and maximum marks
- the median mark
- the lower and upper quartiles of the marks

b) Use your results to represent the singer's marks on a box plot.

c) This box plot shows the marks awarded to the impressionist.

What can you say about the marks awarded to the two acts?

Cumulative Frequency

Q1 Using the cumulative frequency
graph, read off the:

  a) median
  b) lower quartile
  c) upper quartile
  d) interquartile range.

> Cumulative frequency graphs
> show how many data values are
> <u>less than</u> each value on the *x*-axis.

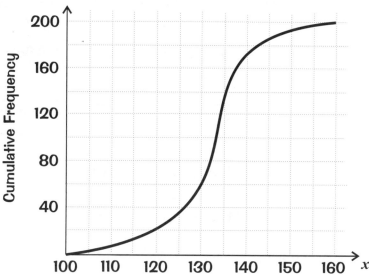

Q2 The number of passengers using a bus service each day has been recorded
over a 4-week period. The data is presented in the table below:

Number of passengers, n	$0 \leq n < 50$	$50 \leq n < 100$	$100 \leq n < 150$	$150 \leq n < 200$	$200 \leq n < 250$	$250 \leq n < 300$
Frequency	2	7	10	5	3	1
Cumulative Frequency						
Mid-Interval						
Frequency × Mid-Interval						

  a) By completing the table, estimate the mean number of passengers.
  b) By plotting a cumulative frequency graph, determine the median value.
  c) What is the modal group?

> With cumulative frequency you always
> plot the <u>highest value</u> from each class.

A mean passenger

Q3 40 pupils have taken an exam and their marks are recorded in a frequency table.

Mark (m%)	$0 \leq m < 20$	$20 \leq m < 40$	$40 \leq m < 60$	$60 \leq m < 80$	$80 \leq m < 100$
Frequency	2	12	18	5	3
Cumulative Frequency					

  a) Complete the table and plot the cumulative frequency graph.
  b) What is the value of the lower quartile?
  c) What is the interquartile range?
  d) What is the median mark?
  e) If pupils achieve a certain mark they get a prize. The number of pupils who got a prize
  to those who didn't is in the ratio 3 : 7. Estimate the mark required to get a prize.

Cumulative Frequency

Q4   A crossword tournament has been held. The times (t, in minutes) taken by one hundred people to complete a crossword are presented in the table below.

Time (t, mins)	Frequency	Cumulative frequency
$31 \le t < 41$	4	
$41 \le t < 51$	12	
$51 \le t < 61$	21	
$61 \le t < 71$	32	
$71 \le t < 81$	19	
$81 \le t < 91$	8	
$91 \le t < 101$	4	

a) What is the modal group?

b) Which group contains the median time?

c) By plotting the cumulative frequency graph, estimate the actual value of the median time.

d) Anyone taking more than 75 minutes to complete the crossword is awarded a consolation prize. Estimate how many consolation prizes were awarded.

e) Why might your answer for **d)** not match exactly the number of consolation prizes actually awarded?

Q5   A company that manufactures electric light bulbs records the lifetimes of a sample of 120 bulbs in a grouped frequency table with classes of width 200 hours. The following cumulative frequency graph shows the data that was recorded.

a) Estimate the number of bulbs in the sample that had a lifetime of more than 1300 hours.

b) The company's policy is to say that any bulb with a lifetime of 900 hours or less has failed quality control. Estimate the percentage of bulbs in the sample that failed quality control.

c) The company's managing director claims that 90% of the company's bulbs have a lifetime of more than 1100 hours. Does the data from this sample back up that claim? Explain your answer.

Histograms and Frequency Density

It's the <u>size that counts</u>... You've got to look at the <u>area</u> of the bars to find the frequency. That means looking at the <u>width</u> as well as the height.

Q1 The Bog Snorkelling Appreciation Society conducts a survey on the ages of all their members. The histogram below shows the age distribution of the people surveyed. The Society organises a 'Seniors' bog snorkelling event for members aged 60 or older. Use the graph to estimate the maximum number of people that might take part.

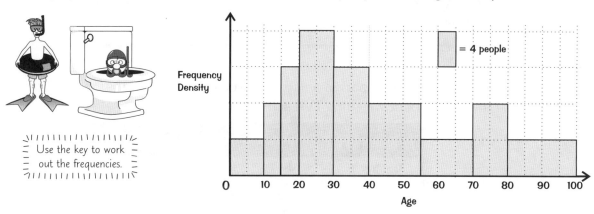

Use the key to work out the frequencies.

Q2 The table below shows the results of a maths test for some Year 11 students. Draw a histogram to represent this information.

Score (x%)	0 < x ≤ 40	40 < x ≤ 60	60 < x ≤ 70	70 < x ≤ 80	80 < x ≤ 100
Frequency	8	14	36	32	10

Q3 A farmer measures the heights of the sunflowers growing in his field. His results are shown in the table and the histogram below.

 a) Use the information in the table and the histogram to number the vertical axis.
 b) Use the histogram to complete the table.
 c) Use the table to add the missing bar to the histogram.

Height (x, in cm)	Frequency
0 < x ≤ 100	50
100 < x ≤ 150	150
150 < x ≤ 200	
200 < x ≤ 220	160
220 < x ≤ 250	90

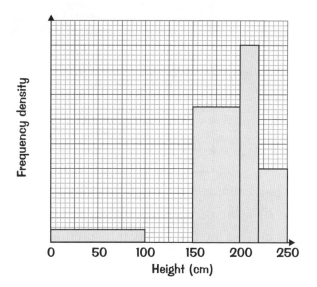

Histograms and Frequency Density

Q4 The weight of honey collected from several beehives is shown in the table below.

a) Complete the frequency table by calculating the frequency densities.

b) Draw a histogram to represent this data.

c) Use your histogram to estimate the number of beehives that produced more than 6 kg of honey.

Weight (w, in kg)	$0 \leq w < 2$	$2 \leq w < 4$	$4 \leq w < 7$	$7 \leq w < 9$	$9 \leq w < 15$
Frequency	3	2	6	9	12
Frequency density					

Q5 A group of students took part in a survey to see how much time they spent watching TV each week.

No. of hours (h)	Frequency	Frequency density
$0 \leq h < 1$	6	
$1 \leq h < 3$	13	
$3 \leq h < 5$	15	
$5 \leq h < 8$	9	
$8 \leq h < 10$	23	
$10 \leq h < 15$	25	
$15 \leq h < 20$	12	

a) Complete the table by filling in the frequency density column.

b) How many students took part in the survey?

c) Write down the modal class.

d) Represent the data as a histogram.

e) Estimate the number of students that watch more than 7 but less than 13 hours each week.

Q6 A farmer keeps track of the amount of milk (*C* litres) produced by his cows each day.

Amount of Milk (C, in litres)	Frequency	Frequency Density	Mid-Interval	Frequency × Mid-Interval
$0 \leq C < 1$	6			
$1 \leq C < 5$	6			
$5 \leq C < 8$	6			
$8 \leq C < 10$	6			
$10 \leq C < 15$	6			
$15 \leq C < 20$	6			

a) Complete the frequency table.

b) Estimate the range of the amounts of milk produced each day.

c) Use the mid-interval technique to estimate the mean.

d) Draw a histogram to show the data.

e) On how many days is less than 7 litres produced?

Histograms and Frequency Density

Q7 A local newspaper employee has collected data on the salaries of
100 people living in the area. His data is shown in the table below.

Salary, S (£1000s)	$0 \leq S < 10$	$10 \leq S < 20$	$20 \leq S < 30$	$30 \leq S < 40$	$40 \leq S < 50$
Frequency	10	25	42	20	3
Frequency Density					

a) Complete the table and draw a histogram to show the data.

b) The newspaper prints this histogram alongside the one
shown on the right. It represents data from an identical
survey done 10 years earlier. Write a comment comparing
current salaries with those from 10 years ago.

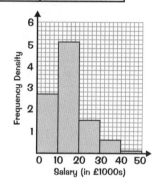

Q8 Mark collected the birth weights (w kg) of each student in his class.
His data is shown in the table below.

Weight at birth (w, in kg)	Number of students
$0 \leq w < 3$	3
$3 \leq w < 3.5$	9
$3.5 \leq w < 4$	11
$4 \leq w < 5$	2

a) Mark drew the histogram on the right
to illustrate his data. Explain what is
wrong with Mark's histogram.

b) Draw an accurate histogram to
represent Mark's data.

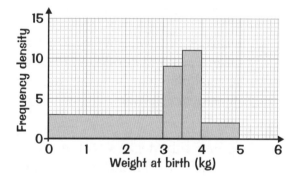

Q9 The histogram on the right shows the test
scores of a year group of 1000 students.

Use the histogram to estimate the mean
test score of the year group.

Instead of using a grouped frequency
table to draw a histogram, you'll
need to use a histogram to make a
grouped frequency table.

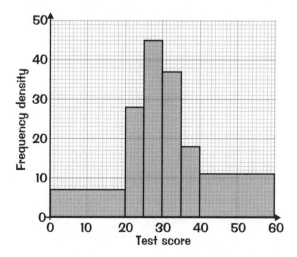

Other Graphs and Charts

Q1 A company that makes pies wants to add a nutritional information diagram to their packaging. Construct a pie chart to show the following nutritional data for one pie:

Contents of Pie	Amount per 100 g
Carbohydrate	35 g
Protein	15 g
Fat	10 g
Magical fairy dust	40 g

When constructing a pie chart, follow the three steps:
1) Find the **TOTAL** represented by the pie chart.
2) Divide 360° by the **TOTAL** to find the **ANGLE** representing 1 unit.
3) Find the angle of each **SECTOR** by multiplying its **FREQUENCY** by the angle representing 1 unit.

Q2 According to the tourist board for the Hindle Isles, 380 000 people visited the biggest island in the group, Sherrington, in 2014. The distribution of tourists for the whole group of islands is shown in the pie chart. Use a protractor on the diagram to find the number of tourists visiting the other islands in 2014 (rounded to the nearest 10 000).

Use the info you're given to find the number of tourists represented by 1°.

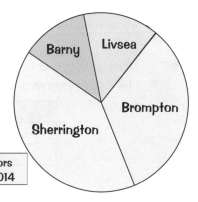

The distribution of visitors to the Hindle Isles in 2014

Q3 Megan records whether customers choose pizza or pasta in her Italian restaurant. The dual bar chart below shows the results over one week.

a) On which days was pizza more popular with Megan's customers?
b) On which day did she have the most customers?
c) Calculate the mean number of customers per day that ordered pizza.

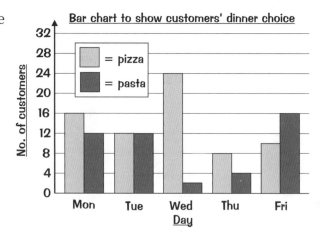

Bar chart to show customers' dinner choice
= pizza
= pasta
No. of customers
Day

Q4 The pie charts opposite appear in a newspaper article about a local election. Nicki says that more people voted for the Green party in 2010 than in 2005.

Comment on whether it's possible to tell this from the pie charts.

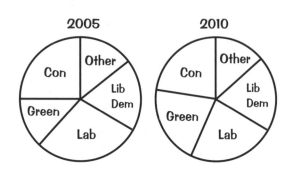

2005   2010

Other Graphs and Charts

Q5 The graphs below show some statistics on marital status for people over 65 years old.

Marital status of people aged 65 and over: by sex and age, 2001

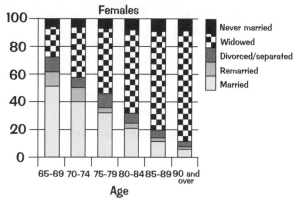

a) What percentage of males aged 65-69 are married?

b) What percentage of females aged 70-74 have remarried?

> These are a bit like bar charts where the bars have been broken down into chunks. Use the vertical axis to find the size of each chunk.

Q6 The table below shows the amount spent on sun cream each season by a British actor living in Hollywood over four years.

Season	Spring 2011	Summer 2011	Autumn 2011	Winter 2011	Spring 2012	Summer 2012	Autumn 2012	Winter 2012
Amount spent ($)	20	27	24	12	22	29	26	21
Season	Spring 2013	Summer 2013	Autumn 2013	Winter 2013	Spring 2014	Summer 2014	Autumn 2014	Winter 2014
Amount spent ($)	25	30	28	20	25	33	31	14

a) Plot the data from the table above in a time-series plot.
b) State the period of the data.
c) Plot a suitable set of moving averages on the graph, and describe the trend in the data.

Q7 Having seen the time-series graph shown here, a Quality Control Manager said:

"Admittedly we do have some complaints about our products, but from July the number of complaints has stopped rising, meaning our products must be of a better quality."

From the graph, do you think this statement is correct? Why/Why not?

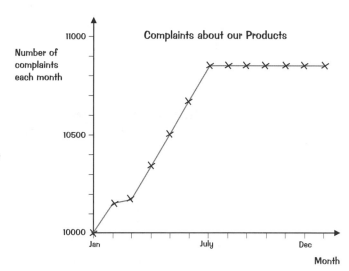

Scatter Graphs

Q1 8 friends are comparing heights and shoe sizes to see if they are correlated.
The data is shown below:

Height	135 cm	140 cm	150 cm	155 cm	165 cm	180 cm	200 cm	215 cm
Shoe size	4	5	4.5	5	6	8	9	12

a) Plot the points on a scatter graph.
b) Describe any correlation you notice between the variables.
c) Write a statement to describe the nature of the relationship between height and shoe size.
d) By fitting an appropriate line, estimate the shoe size of another friend who is 190 cm.

> To draw a scatter graph, just plot one of the variables on the horizontal axis and the other on the vertical axis.

Q2 10 people took 2 exams in Welding for Beginners. The table shows the marks obtained.

Candidate	1	2	3	4	5	6	7	8	9	10
Exam 1 (%)	85	30	55	10	40	20	0	95	65	40
Exam 2 (%)	70	25	50	15	70	25	5	80	60	35

a) Draw a scatter graph representing this information.
b) Draw a line of best fit.
c) Identify the candidate whose scores lead to an outlier on your scatter graph.
d) Clive only sat the first exam, obtaining a mark of 50%. Use your scatter graph to estimate the mark that he might have achieved on the second exam.

Q3 Janine is convinced that cookery books that are more expensive contain more pages. To test out her theory, she has compiled this table:

Price	£4.25	£5.00	£4.75	£6.25	£7.50	£8.25	£4.75	£5.00	£6.75	£3.25	£3.75
No. of pages	204	220	118	184	196	328	158	96	144	84	48

a) Draw a scatter graph to represent this information.
b) Draw in a line of best fit on your scatter graph.
c) Describe the correlation between the price of a cookery book and the number of pages it contains.
d) Use your line to estimate the price of a book containing 250 pages.
e) Explain why using your line to estimate the price of a book containing 450 pages may lead to an unreliable result.

Q4 A local electrical store has kept a log of the number of CD players sold at each price:

Price (£)	£80	£150	£230	£310	£380	£460
No. Sold	27	24	22	19	17	15

a) Draw this information as a scatter graph, using suitable axes.
b) Draw a line of best fit and use it to estimate:
  i) the number of CD players the shopkeeper could expect to sell for £280
  ii) how much the shopkeeper should charge if he wanted to sell exactly 25 CD players.
c) Describe the correlation between the price of a CD player and the number sold.

Answers

Section One — Number

Page 1 — Types of Number and BODMAS

Q1 4

Q2 5, -87, 167

Q3
a) $\sqrt[3]{25}$ = 2.92401..., irrational
b) $\sqrt{16}$ = 4, rational
c) $\sqrt{5}$ = 2.23606..., irrational
d) 3 ÷ 8 = 0.375, rational
e) $8.4\dot{2}$ = 8.42222..., rational
f) Rational

Q4
a) the third cube number (27)
b) the fourth square number (16)

Q5
a) 2
b) e.g. 29
c) 19
d) 19 and 2
e) e.g. 1 or 25

Q6 There's just one: 2 is the only even prime.

Q7 113

Q8
a) 15
b) 4
c) 29
d) 18
e) 4
f) 5
g) 17
h) 4

Q9 $\frac{1}{6}$

Q10 6^2 = 36, 3^3 = 27, prime number = 37 and $10 \times \sqrt{2 \times 5 + 6}$ = 40.
So $10 \times \sqrt{2 \times 5 + 6}$ has the largest value.

Pages 2-3 — Multiples, Factors and Prime Factors

Q1
a) 12
b) 3
c) 1, 9
d) 1, 3, 9
e) P = 12, Q = 6

Q2 Any 5 of:
2 groups of 24, 3 groups of 16,
4 groups of 12, 6 groups of 8,
8 groups of 6, 12 groups of 4,
16 groups of 3, 24 groups of 2.

Q3 The Conversational French and Woodturning classes both have a prime number of students and so cannot be divided into equal groups.

Q4
a) 1, 8, 27, 64, 125
b) 8, 64
c) 27
d) 8, 64
e) 125

Q5
a) 2×3^2
b) $2^2 \times 5 \times 7$
c) $2^2 \times 11$
d) 3^4
e) $2 \times 5^2 \times 11$
f) $2^4 \times 5 \times 7$
g) $2^5 \times 3^2$
h) $2^3 \times 13$

Q6
a) $2 \times 3 \times 5^2 \times 7$
b) $2^2 \times 3^2 \times 5 \times 11$
c) $2 \times 3 \times 7 \times 13$
d) $2^2 \times 3^2 \times 5 \times 7$
e) $2 \times 3 \times 7 \times 11$
f) $2^3 \times 5 \times 7 \times 11$

Q7
a) 2, 3, 5, 7, 11
b) 28
c) $2^2 \times 7$

Q8
a) 495
b) $3 \times 5 \times 11$

Q9
a) 1, 4, 9, 16, 25, 36, 49, 64, 81, 100
b) 4, 16, 36, 64, 100
c) 9, 36, 81
d) 1, 64
e) Total = 385 = 5 × 7 × 11

Q10
a) 50 × 25 × 16 = 20 000 cm³
b) $2^5 \times 5^4$
c) 200. It is not enough to divide the large volume by the smaller volume as the shapes of the blocks are important too. It is possible to fit 16 ÷ 4 = 4 small blocks across the width, 50 ÷ 5 = 10 small blocks along the length and 25 ÷ 5 = 5 small blocks down the height of the large block. This enables Gordon to fit 4 × 10 × 5 = 200 small blocks into the big block.

Q11
a) 680
b) $2^2 \times 5 \times 17$
c) $2 \times 5 \times 17$
d) 5×17

Q12 42

Page 4 — LCM and HCF

Q1
a) 6, 12, 18, 24, 30, 36, 42, 48, 54, 60
b) 5, 10, 15, 20, 25, 30, 35, 40, 45, 50
c) 30

Q2
a) 1, 2, 3, 5, 6, 10, 15, 30
b) 1, 2, 3, 4, 6, 8, 12, 16, 24, 48
c) 6

Q3
a) 20
b) 10
c) 2
d) 15
e) 15
f) 5
g) 32
h) 16
i) 16

Q4
a) 120
b) 120
c) 120
d) 45
e) 90
f) 180
g) 64
h) 192
i) 192

Q5
a) 15 = 3 × 5
18 = 2 × 3²
b) 2 × 3 × 3 × 5 = 90

Q6
a) 90 = 2 × 3² × 5
120 = 2³ × 3 × 5
b) 2 × 3 × 5 = 30

Q7
a) $2^4 \times 3^2$ = 144
b) $2^2 \times 3^2 \times 5 \times 7$ = 1260

Q8
a) 2 × 3 × 5 = 30
b) $2^2 \times 5$ = 20

Q9
a) 7th June (i.e. 6 days later, since 6 is the LCM of 2 and 3)
b) 16th June (i.e. 15 days later, since 15 is the LCM of 3 and 5)
c) Sunday (30 days later, since 30 is the LCM of 2, 3 and 5 — i.e. 4 weeks and 2 days later)
d) Lars (it's 14 days after 1st June, and 14 is a multiple of 2 but not 3 and 5)

Q10 HCF of 36, 42 and 84 is 6.
36 ÷ 6 = 6, 42 ÷ 6 = 7, 84 ÷ 6 = 14
6 + 7 + 14 = 27 friends

Pages 5-6 — Fractions

Q1
a) $\frac{1}{64}$
b) $\frac{3}{88}$
c) $\frac{1}{18}$
d) $\frac{125}{32}$
e) $\frac{1}{10}$
f) $\frac{81}{100\,000}$

Q2
a) 1
b) 4
c) $\frac{1}{2}$
d) $\frac{2}{5}$
e) $\frac{10}{33}$
f) 1000

Q3
a) $\frac{1}{4}$
b) $\frac{5}{6}$
c) $\frac{73}{60}$
d) $\frac{35}{8}$
e) $\frac{131}{20}$
f) $\frac{83}{60}$

Q4 The bowl will be big enough (since she will make $3\frac{7}{15}$ litres of punch).

Q5
a) $\frac{5}{8}$
b) $\frac{1}{2}$
c) $\frac{5}{12}$
d) $\frac{15}{8}$
e) $-\frac{139}{40}$
f) $\frac{233}{300}$

Q6
a) $\frac{3}{4}$
b) $\frac{5}{12}$
c) $\frac{7}{15}$
d) $4\frac{3}{4}$
e) 4
f) $1\frac{1}{5}$
g) $\frac{5}{8}$
h) $-\frac{1}{24}$
i) $4\frac{3}{5}$
j) $1\frac{1}{30}$
k) 1
l) $\frac{44}{75}$

Q7
a) $\frac{1}{12}$
b) $\frac{1}{4}$
c) $\frac{2}{3}$

Q8
a) Each box will hold 16 sandwiches. So 5 boxes will be needed for 80 sandwiches.
b) 25 inches tall

Q9 10 lambs (= $160 \times \frac{5}{32} \times \frac{2}{5}$)

Q10 6.4 g

Q11
a) $\frac{7}{15} = \frac{63}{135}$, $\frac{4}{9} = \frac{60}{135}$ and $\frac{13}{27} = \frac{65}{135}$.
So Rebekah has the biggest discount.
b) £22.20

Q12
a) 100 g flour
b) 350 g
c) $\frac{2}{7}$
d) 300 g

Q13 Shaded area of C = shaded area of A + unshaded area of B
Unshaded area of B = $1 - \frac{3}{8} = \frac{5}{8}$
So shaded area of C = $\frac{1}{9} + \frac{5}{8} = \frac{53}{72}$

Pages 7-8 — Fractions, Decimals and Percentages

Q1
a) 25%
b) 50%
c) 75%
d) 10%
e) 41.52%
f) 84.06%
g) 6%
h) 28.28%

Q2
a) 0.5
b) 0.12
c) 0.4
d) 0.34
e) 0.602
f) 0.08
g) 0.431
h) 0.068

Q3
a) 50%
b) 12.5%
c) 75%
d) 125%
e) 40%
f) 4%
g) 55%
h) 4.5%

Q4
a) 1/4
b) 3/5
c) 9/20
d) 3/10
e) 3/40
f) 62/125
g) 443/500
h) 81/250

Q5 **a)** 46.15% **d)** 128.57%
b) 16.67% **e)** 27.27%
c) 26.67% **f)** 366.67%

Q6 85%

Q7 Grade 6

Q8 **a)** 0.3 **e)** 1.75
b) 0.37 **f)** 0.68
c) 0.4 **g)** 0.6
d) 0.375 **h)** 0.05

Q9

0.5	0.2	0.125	1.6	0.25	3.5	0.15	0.45
1/2	1/5	1/8	8/5	1/4	7/2	3/20	9/20

Q10 **a)** $0.8\dot{3}$ **e)** $0.9\dot{0}$
b) $0.\dot{7}$ **f)** $0.8\dot{7}$
c) $0.\dot{6}\dot{3}$ **g)** $0.47\dot{8}$
d) $0.4\dot{7}$ **h)** $0.589\dot{1}$

Q11 **a)** $\frac{3}{5}$ **d)** $\frac{16}{125}$ **g)** $\frac{1}{9}$
b) $\frac{3}{4}$ **e)** $\frac{1}{3}$ **h)** $\frac{16}{99}$
c) $\frac{19}{20}$ **f)** $\frac{2}{3}$

Q12 **a)** $\frac{2}{9}$ **d)** $\frac{80}{99}$ **g)** $\frac{251}{333}$
b) $\frac{4}{9}$ **e)** $\frac{4}{33}$ **h)** $\frac{52}{333}$
c) $\frac{8}{9}$ **f)** $\frac{545}{999}$

Q13 **a)** $\frac{2}{15}$ **d)** $\frac{121}{900}$ **g)** $\frac{16}{75}$
b) $\frac{71}{90}$ **e)** $\frac{428}{495}$ **h)** $\frac{6397}{9990}$
c) $\frac{4}{45}$ **f)** $\frac{1}{165}$

Page 9 — Rounding Numbers

Q1 **a)** 62.2 **f)** 3.142
b) 62.19 **g)** 740.00
c) 62.194 **h)** 54.051
d) 19.62433 **i)** 5.889
e) 6.300

Q2 **a)** 1330 **d)** 100
b) 1330 **e)** 0.02
c) 1329.6 **f)** 0.02409

Q3 **a)** 457.0 **d)** 457
b) 456.99 **e)** 460
c) 456.987 **f)** 500

Q4 **a)** £1100 **d)** £3
b) £88 **e)** £376
c) £300 **f)** £44

Q5 23 kg **Q6** 2.35 m
Q7 4.7 m **Q8** £19
Q9 £4.77 **Q10** 1820 g

Page 10 — Estimating

Q1 Mark's tank is roughly $30 \times 15 \times 10$
$= 4500 \text{ cm}^3$, so it won't be big enough.

Q2 **a)** E.g. $6600 \times 2 \approx 6500 \times 2 = 13\,000$
b) E.g. $40 \times 1.4 \times 5 \approx 40 \times 1.5 \times 5 = 300$
c) E.g. $45 \div 9 = 5$
d) E.g. $35\,000 \div 7000 = 5$
e) E.g. $\frac{55 \times 20}{9} \approx \frac{55 \times 20}{10} = 55 \times 2 = 110$
f) E.g. $\frac{150 + 50}{150 - 50} = \frac{200}{100} = 2$
g) E.g. $\frac{820 - 220}{1 + 9} = \frac{600}{10} = 60$

h) E.g. $\frac{80 \times 300}{60 \div 20} = \frac{24000}{3} = 8000$
i) E.g. $\frac{1300 \div 2}{5 \times 10} = \frac{650}{50} = 13$
j) E.g. $3 \div 3 = 1$

Q3 Approximately $15\,000 - (1500 + 2500 + 1500 + 1500 + 3000) = 5000$

Q4 **a)** E.g. $\frac{20 \times 10}{\sqrt{400}} = \frac{200}{20} = 10$
b) E.g. $\frac{10^2 \div 10}{4 \times 5} = \frac{10}{20} = 0.5$
c) E.g. $\frac{6 \times 9}{0.3} = \frac{54}{0.3} = \frac{540}{3} = 180$
d) E.g. $\frac{\sqrt{100}}{0.3 + 0.2} = \frac{10}{0.5} = 20$

Q5 **a)** $2 \times (3 \times 3) + 2 \times (3 \times 3) = 36 \text{ m}^2$
b) 3 tins

Q6 **a)** Volume $\approx 3 \times 5^2 \times 20 = 1500 \text{ cm}^3$
E.g. Larger than actual volume — the estimate treats the vase as a cylinder, but the vase curves inwards, so the actual volume is smaller. The height is also rounded up in the estimate.
b) Volume $\approx 3 \times 2^2 \times 10 = 120 \text{ cm}^3$
E.g. Larger than actual volume — glass is treated as a cylinder whose diameter is equal to the widest part of the glass. The height has also been rounded up.

Q7 **a)** 6.9 (accept 6.8)
b) 10.9 (accept 10.8)
c) 9.2 (accept 9.1)
d) 4.1 (accept 4.2)
e) 2.2 (accept 2.1)
f) 2.9 (accept 2.8)

Pages 11-12 — Bounds

Q1 **a)** 64.785 kg **b)** 64.775 kg
Q2 **a)** 1.75 m
b) $1.85 \times 0.75 = 1.3875 \text{ m}^2$
Q3 **a)** $300.6 \text{ m} \leq h < 300.7 \text{ m}$
b) 125 m
Q4 **a)** 2.525 l **b)** 2.475 l
Q5 **a)** $85 \text{ g} \leq p < 95 \text{ g}$
b) $92.5 \text{ g} \leq p < 97.5 \text{ g}$
c) No — the lower bound for the post office scales is 97.5 g. This value doesn't fall within the interval for either of the other two scales.
Q6 **a)** Upper bound = 127, lower bound = 123
b) No — the minimum number of people attending is 128, and the maximum number of chairs is 127.
Q7 **a)** Upper bound = 5 minutes 32.5 seconds, lower bound = 5 minutes 27.5 seconds.
b) The lower bound for Jimmy's time is 5 minutes 25 seconds, which is lower than the lower bound for Douglas' time (5 minutes 25.5 seconds).
Q8 **a)** Upper bound = 13.5, lower bound = 12.5
b) Upper bound = 12.55, lower bound = 12.45
c) To calculate the upper bound for C, multiply the upper bound for A by the upper bound for B:

$13.5 \times 12.55 = 169.425$
To calculate the lower bound for C, multiply the lower bound for A by the lower bound for B:
$12.5 \times 12.45 = 155.625$
$155.625 \leq C < 169.425$

Q9 No — Ash will buy $3.45 \text{ m} \times 5.25 \text{ m} = 18.1125 \text{ m}^2$.

Q10 **a)** Perimeter $= 2(12 + 4) = 32$ cm.
Maximum possible error $= 4 \times 0.1$ cm $= 0.4$ cm.
b) Maximum possible error in P is $2(x + y)$.

Q11 The upper bound for the distance is 127.5 km. The lower bound for the time is 1 hour and 45 minutes = 1.75 hours. The maximum value of the average speed is $127.5 \div 1.75 = 72.857\ldots$ km/hour.

Q12 **a)** Upper bound = 945, lower bound = 935.
b) Upper bound = 5.565, lower bound = 5.555.
c) To find the upper bound for R, divide the upper bound for S by the lower bound for T:
$945 \div 5.555 = 170.117\ldots$
To find the lower bound for R, divide the lower bound for S by the upper bound for T:
$935 \div 5.565 = 168.014\ldots$
d) $R = 170$ to 2 s.f. (as both upper and lower bounds round to 170 to 2 s.f.).

Pages 13-14 — Standard Form

Q1 **a)** 35.6 **b)** 3560
c) 0.356 **d)** 35 600
e) 8.2 **f)** 0.00082
g) 0.82 **h)** 0.0082
i) 1570 **j)** 0.157
k) 157 000 **l)** 15.7

Q2 **a)** 2.56×10^0 **b)** 2.56×10^1
c) 2.56×10^{-1} **d)** 2.56×10^4
e) 9.52×10^1 **f)** 9.52×10^{-2}
g) 9.52×10^4 **h)** 9.52×10^{-4}
i) 4.2×10^3 **j)** 4.2×10^{-3}
k) 4.2×10^1 **l)** 4.2×10^2

Q3 **a)** 3.47×10^2 **b)** 7.3004×10^1
c) 5×10^0 **d)** 9.183×10^5
e) 1.5×10^7 **f)** 9.371×10^6
g) 7.5×10^{-5} **h)** 5×10^{-4}
i) 5.34×10^0 **j)** 6.2103×10^2
k) 1.49×10^4 **l)** 3×10^{-7}

Q4 1.2×10^{-2} mm

Q5 **a)** Mercury
b) Jupiter
c) Mercury
d) Neptune
e) Venus and Mercury
f) Jupiter, Neptune and Saturn

Q6 **a)** 4.2×10^7 **b)** 3.8×10^{-4}
c) 1.0×10^7 **d)** 1.12×10^{-4}
e) 8.43×10^5 **f)** 4.232×10^{-3}
g) 1.7×10^{18} **h)** 2.83×10^{-4}
i) 1.0×10^{-2}

Q7 **a)** 1.89×10^7 **d)** 3.99×10^4
b) 2×10^2 **e)** 4.1×10^5
c) 7.36×10^{13} **f)** 1.28×10^4

Q8 a) 9.12×10^9 c) 3.363×10^6
b) 5.8×10^1 d) 4.3473×10^6

Q9 a) 2.4×10^{10} c) 1.8×10^5
b) 1.6×10^6

Q10 1.04×10^{13} is greater by 5.78×10^{12}

Q11 1.3×10^{-9} is smaller by 3.07×10^{-8}

Q12 a) $510\,000\,000$ km^2
b) 3.62×10^8 km^2
c) $148\,000\,000$ km^2

Q13 a) $(2 \times 5)^{15} \times 5^2 = 25 \times 10^{15} = 2.5 \times 10^{16}$
b) $2^1 \times (2 \times 5)^{-21} = 2 \times 10^{-21}$
c) $\dfrac{1}{2^3 \times (2 \times 5)^{-2}} = \dfrac{1}{8 \times 10^{-2}} = 1.25 \times 10^1$

Q14 $x = 4$, $y = 2$, $z = 1$

Q15 a) 4.2×10^3 c) 3×10^3
b) 5.1×10^{26} d) 5.2×10^{-24}

Q16 a) $6.02 \times 10^{23} \approx 6 \times 10^{23}$
$12 \div (6 \times 10^{23}) = 2 \times 10^{-23}$ g
b) smaller

Section Two — Algebra

Page 15 — Algebra Basics

Q1 a) -27 °C d) $+18$ °C
b) -22 °C e) $+15$ °C
c) $+12$ °C f) -12 °C

Q2 Expression **b)** is larger by 7.

Q3 a) $6x$ b) $28y$

Q4 a) $-1000, -10$ c) $144, 16$
b) $-96, -6$ d) $0, 0$

Q5 -4

Q6 a) $-6xy$ e) $\dfrac{10x}{y}$ i) -4
b) $-16ab$ f) $\dfrac{-10x}{y}$ j) -10
c) $8x^2$ g) $\dfrac{-5x}{y}$ k) $4x$
d) $-16p^2$ h) 3 l) $-8y$

Q7 a) $15x^2 - x$
b) $13x^2 - 5x$
c) $-7x^2 + 12x + 12$
d) $30abc + 12ab + 4b$
e) $18pq + 8p$
f) $17ab - 17a + b$
g) $4pq - 5p - 9q$
h) $16x^2 - 4y^2$
i) $abc + 10ab - 11cd$
j) $-2x^2 + y^2 - z^2 + 6xy$

Q8 a) $x^2 + 4x + 3x + 12 = x^2 + 7x + 12$
b) $4x^2 + 6x + 6x + 9 = 4x^2 + 12x + 9$
c) $15x^2 + 3x + 10x + 2$
$= 15x^2 + 13x + 2$

Pages 16-17 — Powers and Roots

Q1 a) 16
b) 1000
c) $3 \times 3 \times 3 \times 3 \times 3 = 243$
d) $1 \times 1 \times 1 \times 1 \times 1 \times 1 \times 1 \times 1 \times 1 = 1$

Q2 a) 2^8 (or 256) c) m^3
b) 12^5 (or $248\,832$) d) z^6

Q3 b) 10^7 c) 10^8
d) Simply add the powers.

Q4 b) 2^3 c) 4^2
d) 8^3
e) Simply subtract the powers.

Q5 a) true g) false
b) true h) true
c) false i) false
d) false j) true
e) true k) true
f) false l) false

Q6 a) true b) false c) false

Q7 a) 3^{-3} g) 2^3
b) 4^{25} h) 10^{10}
c) 10^{-13} i) 7^{20}
d) 3^{-12} j) $3^{\frac{2}{3}}$
e) 4^6 k) $4^{-\frac{1}{4}}$
f) 5^3 l) $2^{\frac{5}{3}}$

Q8 a) x^5 g) $30b^{-5}$ l) $11c^{-5}d^{-6}$
b) y h) $9x^6y^8$ m) $28a^3b$
c) a^{12} i) $6a^8b^5$ n) $12x^4$
d) f^5 j) $8p^{-2}q^{-11}$ o) x^2
e) 1 k) $2x^2y^3$ p) $3y^{-\frac{1}{5}}$
f) $\dfrac{8x^7}{y^3}$

Q9 a) 275 g) 10.4
b) 0.123 h) 0.843
c) $53\,400$ i) 2.25
d) 6.40×10^{-5} j) 2.18
e) 2.37 k) 0.244
f) 2.31 l) 0.965

Q10 a) 8.76 f) 91.9
b) 4.17 g) 13.6
c) 19.4 h) 17.8
d) 219 i) 5.06
e) 108

Q11 a) 0.204 g) 1.55
b) 0.16 h) 2.60
c) 1.53×10^{-5} i) 0.512
d) 0.667 j) 1.21
e) 2.24 k) 0.0352
f) 1.82 l) 7.28

Q12 a) 1.49 e) 1.08
b) 20.1 f) 8.78
c) 2.50 g) 0.707
d) 6.55 h) -0.380

Q13 a) 9.14 f) 1.22
b) 1.50 g) 84.5
c) 0.406 h) 0.496
d) 476 i) 165
e) 0.0146 j) 8.47

Q14 a) 2 e) 512
b) 7 f) 8
c) $\dfrac{1}{9}$ g) $\dfrac{1}{3}$
d) $\dfrac{1}{64}$ h) $\dfrac{5}{9}$

Page 18 — Multiplying Out Brackets

Q1 a) $4x + 4y - 4z$
b) $x^2 + 5x$
c) $-3x + 6$
d) $9a + 9b$
e) $-a + 4b$
f) $2x - 6$
g) $4e^2 - 2f^2 + 10ef$
h) $16m - 8n$
i) $6x^2 + 2x$
j) $-2ab + 11$
k) $-2x^3 - x^2z - 2yz$
l) $3x^2 - 6y - 5$
m) $-3a - 4b$
n) $14pqr^3 + 8pq + 35qr^3$
o) $x^3 + x^2$
p) $4x^3 + 8x^2 + 4x$
q) $8a^4b + 24ab + 8ab^2$
r) $7p^2q + 7pq^2 - 7q$
s) $16x - 8y$

Q2 a) $x^2 - 2x - 3$
b) $x^2 + 2x - 15$
c) $x^2 + 13x + 30$
d) $x^2 - 7x + 10$
e) $x^2 - 5x - 14$
f) $28 - 11x + x^2$
g) $6x - 2 + 9x^2 - 3x = 9x^2 + 3x - 2$
h) $6x^2 - 12x + 4x - 8 = 6x^2 - 8x - 8$
i) $4x^2 + \sqrt{2}x - 4\sqrt{2}x - 2$
$= 4x^2 - 3\sqrt{2}x - 2$
j) $4x^2 - 8xy + 2xy - 4y^2$
$= 4x^2 - 4y^2 - 6xy$
k) $12x^2 - 8xy + 24xy - 16y^2$
$= 12x^2 - 16y^2 + 16xy$
l) $9x^2 + 6xy + 6xy + 4y^2$
$= 9x^2 + 4y^2 + 12xy$
m) $4a^2 - 2ab - 2ab + b^2$
$= 4a^2 + b^2 - 4ab$
n) $t^2 + 2\sqrt{2}t - 2\sqrt{2}t - 8$
$= t^2 - 8$
o) $9p^2 + 3\sqrt{2}p + 3\sqrt{2}p + 2$
$= 9p^2 + 6\sqrt{2}p + 2$

Q3 $15x^2 + 10x - 6x - 4 = 15x^2 + 4x - 4$

Q4 $4x^2 - 2x - 2x + 1 = 4x^2 - 4x + 1$

Q5 a) $x^3 + x^2 - 4x - 4$
b) $x^3 + 10x^2 + 31x + 30$
c) $2x^3 - 15x^2 + 27x - 10$
d) $-x^3 - 4x^2 + 11x + 30$
e) $-2x^3 - 7x^2 - 2x + 3$
f) $6x^3 + 74x^2 + 144x + 40$
g) $-x^3 - 3x^2 + 9x + 27$
h) $4x^3 - 3x - 1$
i) $x^3 + 9x^2 + 27x + 27$

Q6 a) $(4x + 6)$ m
b) $(-3x^2 + 17x - 10)$ m^2

Q7 a) $(4 + 2x)$ cm or $2(2 + x)$ cm
b) $(40x + 80)$ cm

Q8 a) Perimeter — $(3x + 29)$ cm
Area — $\dfrac{7x + 126}{2}$ cm^2
or $(3.5x + 63)$ cm^2
b) Perimeter — $(8x + 4)$ cm
Area — $(3x^2 + 14x - 24)$ cm^2
c) Perimeter — $(16x - 4)$ cm
Area — $(16x^2 - 8x + 1)$ cm^2
d) Perimeter — $(10x + 4)$ cm
Area — $(6x^2 - 5x - 6)$ cm^2

Page 19 — Factorising

Q1 a) $a^2(b + c)$
b) $a^2(5 + 13b)$
c) $a^2(2b + 3c)$
d) $a^2(a + y)$
e) $a^2(2x + 3y + 4z)$
f) $a^2(b^2 + ac^2)$

Q2 a) $x(x - 5)$
b) $2(x + 3)$
c) $3x(x + 4)$
d) $2x(2x - 3)$
e) $3xy(1 + 4x)$
f) $3(3x + 5)$
g) $5x(3xy - 5)$

h) $4pq(q - 5 + 2p)$

i) $2x(5x^3 + 3)$

j) $5x^2(3x - 4)$

k) $7x(3x + 2)$

l) $5xy(z + 4u)$

Q3 a) $4x(1 + 2yz)$

b) $4x^2(2xy + 3z)$

c) $8xyz(1 + 2x)$

d) $4xyz^2(5xy + 4)$

Q4 a) $(x + 3)(x - 3)$

b) $(y + 4)(y - 4)$

c) $(5 + z)(5 - z)$

d) $(6 + a)(6 - a)$

e) $(2x + 3)(2x - 3)$

f) $(3y + 2)(3y - 2)$

g) $(5 + 4z)(5 - 4z)$

h) $(1 + 6a)(1 - 6a)$

i) $(x^2 + 6)(x^2 - 6)$

j) $(x^2 + y^2)(x^2 - y^2)$

k) $(1 + ab)(1 - ab)$

l) $(10x + 12y)(10x - 12y)$

Q5 a) $(x + 2)(x - 2)$

b) $(12 + y^2)(12 - y^2)$

c) $(1 + 3xy)(1 - 3xy)$

d) $(7x^2y^2 + 1)(7x^2y^2 - 1)$

e) $3(x + 2)(x - 2)$

f) $10(3 + y)(3 - y)$

g) $2(5x + 4)(5x - 4)$

h) $5(2 + 3xy)(2 - 3xy)$

Q6 a) $(x + \sqrt{3})(x - \sqrt{3})$

b) $(3x + \sqrt{5})(3x - \sqrt{5})$

c) $(x + \sqrt{7}y)(x - \sqrt{7}y)$

d) $(\sqrt{2} + xy)(\sqrt{2} - xy)$

Q7 a) $16a^2b^2(4b - a)$

b) $q(p + r - pqr)$

c) $3(m^2 - 8)$

d) $b^2(b^2 - ab + c)$

e) $(a^2 + 13)(a^2 - 13)$

f) $3ab(3b - c)$

g) $(9 + z)(9 - z)$

h) $(11p + 3q)(11p - 3q)$

i) $mn(m + 3 - 2n^2)$

j) $2(6m + 5n)(6m - 5n)$

k) $12(12x^2 - 9y^2 - 5z^2)$

l) $(8ab + 7cd)(8ab - 7cd)$

Page 20 — Manipulating Surds

Q1 a) $\sqrt{15}$ b) 2

c) x d) x

e) 8   f) $\sqrt{5}$

Q2 3π cm^2

Q3 a) 1   b) $5\sqrt{3}$

c) $2\sqrt{2}$ d) $7 + 4\sqrt{3}$

e) $3\sqrt{5}$ f) $5\sqrt{2}$

g) $\sqrt{2}$ h) $3(\sqrt{2} - 1)$

Q4 a) $\dfrac{\sqrt{2}}{2}$ b) $\dfrac{\sqrt{10}a}{10}$

c) $\dfrac{\sqrt{xy}}{y}$ d) $3 - \sqrt{3}$

e) $\dfrac{2(\sqrt{6} - 1)}{5}$ f) $\dfrac{3 + \sqrt{5}}{2}$

g) $\dfrac{15 + 11\sqrt{3}}{6}$ h) $\dfrac{34 + \sqrt{6}}{50}$

Q5 a) $6\sqrt{7}$ b) $8\sqrt{3}$ c) $28\sqrt{15}$

d) $\dfrac{11\sqrt{3}}{9}$ e) 0   f) $8\sqrt{5}$

g) $-1 - 2\sqrt{3}$ h) $9 + 4\sqrt{2}$

i) $3 - \sqrt{3}$

Q6 a) $(1 + \sqrt{5})(1 - \sqrt{5}) = -4$, rational

b) $\dfrac{1 + \sqrt{5}}{1 - \sqrt{5}} = -\dfrac{1}{2}(3 + \sqrt{5})$, irrational

Q7 a) $(x + y)(x - y) = 1^2 - \sqrt{2}^2 = -1$, rational

b) $\dfrac{x + y}{x - y} = \dfrac{1 + \sqrt{2}}{1 - \sqrt{2}}$

$= -3 - 2\sqrt{2}$, irrational

Pages 21-22 — Solving Equations

Q1 1

Q2 a) $x = 5$ d) $x = -6$

b) $x = 4$ e) $x = -4$

c) $x = 10$ f) $x = 6$

Q3 a) $x = 5$ d) $x = 17$

b) $x = 2$ e) $x = 6$

c) $x = 8$ f) $x = 5$

Q4 a) 15.5   b) 37.2

Q5 15.50

Q6 a) $x = 9$ g) $x = 15$

b) $x = 2$ h) $x = 110$

c) $x = 3$ i) $x = 66$

d) $x = 3$ j) $x = 700$

e) $x = 4$ k) $x = 7\frac{1}{2}$

f) $x = -1$

Q7 a) Joan — £x

Kate — £$2x$

Linda — £$(x - 232)$

b) $4x - 232 = 2400$

$x = 658$

c) Kate — £1316

Linda — £426

Q8 a) $(2x + 24)$ cm

b) $9x$ cm^2

c) $x = 3.43$ (to 3 s.f.)

Q9 a) $x = 0.75$ d) $x = -1$

b) $x = -1$ e) $x = 4$

c) $x = -6$ f) $x = 13$

Q10 $x = 8$

Q11 $x = 1$

Q12 8 years old

Q13 $x = 39$, wife = 35, son = 8

Q14 $x = 1\frac{1}{2}$

AB = 5 cm

AC = 5½ cm

BC = 7½ cm

Q15 a) $y = 22$ f) $x = 7$

b) $x = 8$ g) $x = 4$

c) $z = -5$ h) $x = 3$

d) $x = 19$ i) $x = 2$

e) $x = 23$

Q16 $x = 1\frac{1}{2}$

Q17 a) $x = 9$ c) $x = 2$

b) $x = 5$ d) $x = 5$

Q18 a) $x = \pm 3$ h) $x = \pm\frac{3}{4}$

b) $x = \pm 6$ i) $x = \pm 2$

c) $x = \pm 3$ j) $x = \pm 6$

d) $x = \pm 3$ k) $x = \pm 3$

e) $x = \pm 1$ l) $x = \pm 4$

f) $x = \pm 2$ m) $x = \pm 7$

g) $x = \pm\frac{2}{3}$

Pages 23-24 — Rearranging Formulas

Q1 a) $h = \dfrac{10 - g}{4}$ e) $g = \dfrac{8f}{3}$

b) $c = 2d - 4$ f) $x = 2(y + 3)$

c) $k = 3 + \dfrac{j}{2}$ g) $t = 6(s - 10)$

d) $b = \dfrac{3a}{2}$ h) $q = \pm\dfrac{\sqrt{p}}{2}$

Q2 a) $c = \dfrac{w - 500m}{50}$

b) 132

Q3 a) i) £38.00   ii) £48.00

b) $c = 28 + 0.25n$

c) $n = 4(c - 28)$

d) i) 24 miles   ii) 88 miles

iii) 114 miles

Q4 a) $x = \pm\sqrt{y + 2}$

b) $x = y^2 - 3$

c) $s = \pm 2\sqrt{r}$

d) $g = 3f - 10$

e) $z = 5 - 2w$

f) $x = \pm\sqrt{\dfrac{3v}{h}}$

g) $a = \dfrac{v^2 - u^2}{2s}$

h) $u = \pm\sqrt{v^2 - 2as}$

i) $g = \dfrac{4\pi^2 l}{t^2}$

Q5 a) £Jx b) $P = T - Jx$

c) $J = \dfrac{T - P}{x}$ d) £16

Q6 a) i) £2.04   ii) £3.48

b) $C = 12x + 60$

c) $x = \dfrac{C - 60}{12}$

d) i) 36   ii) 48   iii) 96

Q7 a) $x = \dfrac{z}{y + 2}$

b) $x = \dfrac{b}{a - 3}$

c) $x = \dfrac{y}{4 - z}$

d) $x = \dfrac{3z + y}{y + 5}$

e) $x = \dfrac{-2}{y - z}$ or $\dfrac{2}{z - y}$

f) $x = \dfrac{2y + 3z}{2 - z}$

g) $x = \dfrac{-y - wz}{yz - 1}$ or $\dfrac{y + wz}{1 - yz}$

h) $x = \dfrac{-z}{4}$

Q8 a) $y = \dfrac{x}{x - 1}$

b) $y = \dfrac{-3 - 2x}{x - 1}$ or $\dfrac{2x + 3}{1 - x}$

c) $y = \dfrac{5x + 3}{2x - 1}$

d) $y = \dfrac{5 - 2x}{5x + 2}$

e) $y = \pm\sqrt{\dfrac{x + 1}{2x - 1}}$

f) $y = \pm\sqrt{\dfrac{1 + 2x}{3x - 2}}$

Q9 a) $p = \dfrac{4r - 2q}{q - 3}$

b) $g = \dfrac{5 - 2e}{f + 2}$

c) $b = \dfrac{3c + 2a}{a - c}$

d) $q = \pm\sqrt{\dfrac{4}{p - r}} = \pm\dfrac{2}{\sqrt{p - r}}$

e) $a = \dfrac{2c + 4b}{4 + c - d}$

f) $x = \pm\sqrt{\dfrac{-3y}{2}}$

g) $k = \pm\sqrt{\dfrac{14}{h - 1}}$

h) $x = \left(\dfrac{4 - y}{2 - z}\right)^2$

i) $a = \dfrac{b^2}{3 + b}$

j) $m = -7n$

k) $e = \dfrac{d}{50}$

l) $y = \dfrac{x}{3x + 2}$

Page 25 — Factorising Quadratics

Q1 **a)** $(x + 5)(x - 2) = 0$
$x = -5, x = 2$
b) $(x - 3)(x - 2) = 0$
$x = 3, x = 2$
c) $(x - 1)^2 = 0$
$x = 1$
d) $(x - 3)(x - 1) = 0$
$x = 3, x = 1$
e) $(x - 5)(x + 4) = 0$
$x = 5, x = -4$
f) $(x + 7)^2 = 0$
$x = -7$
g) $x^2 + x - 12 = 0$
$(x - 3)(x + 4) = 0$
$x = 3, x = -4$
h) $x^2 + 7x - 8 = 0$
$(x - 1)(x + 8) = 0$
$x = 1, x = -8$
i) $x^2 - 2x - 35 = 0$
$(x - 7)(x + 5) = 0$
$x = 7, x = -5$

Q2 **a)** $(x + 1)(2x - 5) = 0$
$x = -1, x = \dfrac{5}{2}$
b) $(3x + 7)(x - 1) = 0$
$x = -\dfrac{7}{3}, x = 1$
c) $(x - 5)(2x + 3) = 0$
$x = 5, x = -\dfrac{3}{2}$
d) $(2x + 3)^2 = 0$
$x = -\dfrac{3}{2}$
e) $(4x - 1)(x + 2) = 0$
$x = \dfrac{1}{4}, x = -2$
f) $(5x - 1)(x - 6) = 0$
$x = \dfrac{1}{5}, x = 6$
g) $3x^2 + x - 2 = 0$
$(3x - 2)(x + 1) = 0$
$x = \dfrac{2}{3}, x = -1$
h) $2x^2 - 9x + 10 = 0$
$(2x - 5)(x - 2) = 0$
$x = \dfrac{5}{2}, x = 2$
i) $9x^2 + 3x - 2 = 0$
$(3x - 1)(3x + 2) = 0$

$x = \dfrac{1}{3}, x = -\dfrac{2}{3}$

Q3 **a)** $(x + 8)(x - 2) = 0$
$x = -8, x = 2$
b) $(x + 9)(x - 4) = 0$
$x = -9, x = 4$
c) $(x + 9)(x - 5) = 0$
$x = -9, x = 5$
d) $x(x - 5) = 0$
$x = 0, x = 5$
e) $x(x - 11) = 0$
$x = 0, x = 11$
f) $(x - 7)(x + 3) = 0$
$x = 7, x = -3$
g) $(x - 30)(x + 10) = 0$
$x = 30, x = -10$
h) $(x - 24)(x - 2) = 0$
$x = 24, x = 2$
i) $(x - 9)(x - 4) = 0$
$x = 9, x = 4$
j) $(x + 7)(x - 2) = 0$
$x = -7, x = 2$
k) $(x + 7)(x - 3) = 0$
$x = -7, x = 3$
l) $(3x - 5)(x + 2) = 0$
$x = \dfrac{5}{3}, x = -2$
m) $(x - 6)(2x + 3) = 0$
$x = 6, x = -\dfrac{3}{2}$
n) $(2x - 5)^2 = 0$
$x = \dfrac{5}{2}$
o) $(3x + 4)(2x - 3) = 0$
$x = -\dfrac{4}{3}, x = \dfrac{3}{2}$

Q4 $x = \dfrac{1}{2}, x = -\dfrac{1}{2}$

Q5 $x = 4$

Q6 **a)** $(x^2 - x)$ m²
b) $x = 3$

Q7 **a)** $(x^2 + x)$ cm²
b) $x = 3$

Q8 **a)** **i)** x^2 m²
ii) $12x$ m²
b) $x^2 + 12x - 64 = 0$
$x = 4$

Pages 26-27 — The Quadratic Formula

Q1 **a)** 1.87, 0.13
b) 2.39, 0.28
c) 1.60, −3.60
d) 1.16, −3.16
e) 0.53, −4.53
f) −11.92, −15.08
g) −2.05, −4.62
h) 0.84, 0.03

Q2 **a)** −2, −6   **j)** 4, −5
b) 0.67, −0.5   **k)** 1, −3
c) 3, −2   **l)** 5, −1.33
d) 2, 1   **m)** 1.5, −1
e) 3, 0.75   **n)** −2.5, 1
f) 3, 0   **o)** 0.5, 0.33
g) 0.67   **p)** 1, −3
h) 0, −2.67   **q)** 2, −6
i) 4, −0.5   **r)** 2, −4

Q3 **a)** 0.30, −3.30   **i)** 7.12, −1.12
b) 3.65, −1.65   **j)** 13.16, 0.84
c) 0.62, −1.62   **k)** 1.19, −4.19
d) −0.55, −5.45   **l)** 1.61, 0.53
e) −0.44, −4.56   **m)** 0.44, −3.44

f) 1.62, −0.62   **n)** 2.78, 0.72
g) 0.67, −4   **o)** −1.23, −2.43
h) −0.59, −3.41

Q4 **a)** $\dfrac{-3 \pm \sqrt{41}}{2}$ **i)** $\dfrac{5 \pm \sqrt{33}}{4}$

b) $-2 \pm \sqrt{3}$ **j)** $\dfrac{7 \pm \sqrt{17}}{4}$

c) $\dfrac{3 \pm \sqrt{69}}{6}$ **k)** $\dfrac{1 \pm \sqrt{2}}{2}$

d) $\dfrac{-4 \pm 3\sqrt{2}}{2}$ **l)** $\dfrac{3 \pm \sqrt{6}}{2}$

e) $2 \pm 2\sqrt{2}$ **m)** $\dfrac{-5 \pm \sqrt{13}}{2}$

f) $\dfrac{1 \pm \sqrt{5}}{2}$ **n)** $\dfrac{-3 \pm \sqrt{3}}{2}$

g) $\dfrac{-1 \pm \sqrt{19}}{3}$ **o)** $\dfrac{-7 \pm 3\sqrt{5}}{2}$

h) $\dfrac{-5 \pm \sqrt{21}}{2}$

Q5 $x^2 - 3.6x + 3.24 = 0$
$x = 1.8$

Q6 **a)** $x^2 + 2.5x - 144.29 = 0$
$x = 10.83$
b) 48.3 cm

Page 28 — Completing the Square

Q1 **a)** $(x - 2)^2 - 9$
b) $(x - 1)^2$
c) $(x + \tfrac{1}{2})^2 + \tfrac{3}{4}$
d) $(x - 3)^2$
e) $(x - 3)^2 - 2$
f) $(x - 2)^2 - 4$
g) $(x + 1\tfrac{1}{2})^2 - 6\tfrac{1}{4}$
h) $(x - \tfrac{1}{2})^2 - 3\tfrac{1}{4}$
i) $(x - 5)^2$
j) $(x - 5)^2 - 25$
k) $(x + 4)^2 + 1$
l) $(x - 6)^2 - 1$

Q2 **a)** $x = 0.30, x = -3.30$
b) $x = 2.30, x = -1.30$
c) $x = 0.65, x = -4.65$
d) $x = 0.62, x = -1.62$
e) $x = 4.19, x = -1.19$
f) $x = 2.82, x = 0.18$
g) $x = 1.46, x = -0.46$
h) $x = 2.15, x = -0.15$

Q3 **a)** $4 \pm \sqrt{29}$
b) $1 \pm \sqrt{6}$
c) $-3 \pm 2\sqrt{5}$
d) $-4 \pm 2\sqrt{3}$
e) $\dfrac{-3 \pm \sqrt{17}}{2}$
f) $\dfrac{-7 \pm \sqrt{37}}{2}$
g) $\dfrac{5 \pm 5\sqrt{5}}{2}$
h) $\dfrac{9 \pm 3\sqrt{5}}{2}$
i) $-1 \pm \dfrac{3\sqrt{2}}{2}$
j) $1 \pm \dfrac{2\sqrt{3}}{3}$
k) $\dfrac{7 \pm \sqrt{73}}{4}$
l) $\dfrac{5 \pm \sqrt{13}}{6}$

Answers

Q4 **a)** $(5, -28)$

b) $\left(\frac{7}{2}, -\frac{109}{4}\right)$

c) $(-2, -10)$

d) $\left(\frac{5}{8}, -\frac{41}{16}\right)$

Q5 **a)** $(-2, -5)$, minimum

b) $\left(\frac{11}{2}, \frac{97}{4}\right)$, maximum

c) $\left(-\frac{3}{2}, \frac{41}{4}\right)$, maximum

d) $(-2, -19)$, minimum

e) $\left(-\frac{5}{4}, -\frac{33}{8}\right)$, minimum

f) $(-1, 5)$, maximum

Q6 **a)**

b)

c)

Q7 $y = \left(x + \frac{m}{2}\right)^2 - \frac{m^2}{4} + n$

This has its turning point when
$x = -\frac{m}{2} = 1$. So $m = -2$.
When $x = 1$, $y = -\frac{m^2}{4} + n = -5$.
So $n = -4$.

Pages 29-30 — Algebraic Fractions

Q1 **a)** $\frac{3xy}{z}$ **c)** $\frac{1}{3xy^2z^3}$

b) $\frac{12b^2}{c}$ **d)** $\frac{q^3}{2r^3}$

Q2 **a)** $\frac{2}{xy}$ **d)** $\frac{x^3}{5}$

b) $\frac{8x^2z^2}{y}$ **e)** $\frac{12a^3b^2}{5}$

c) $\frac{90ac^4}{b}$ **f)** $\frac{d^6}{e^3f}$

Q3 **a)** $2x^2y$ **d)** $\frac{12yz}{x}$

b) $\frac{3x^2}{y}$ **e)** $\frac{2x}{y^2z}$

c) $5x^3$ **f)** $\frac{6}{n}$

Q4 **a)** $\frac{3}{2r}$ **c)** $\frac{m^2 - l^2}{n^2}$

b) $\frac{a^2}{b^2}$

Q5 **a)** $\frac{3a - 4}{2}$ **d)** $\frac{3}{4x - 7}$

b) $\frac{2x - y}{4}$ **e)** $\frac{5}{6a + b}$

c) $\frac{5x + 6}{3}$ **f)** $\frac{4}{5x + 3}$

Q6 **a)** $\frac{x + 2}{x + 3}$ **c)** $\frac{x - 5}{x - 2}$

b) $\frac{x + 1}{x - 3}$ **d)** $\frac{x + 1}{2x - 7}$

Q7 **a)** $\frac{14x + y}{6}$ **g)** $\frac{2x^2 + y + xy}{x^3}$

b) $\frac{x + 2y - 2}{10}$ **h)** $\frac{2(2x + 1)}{(x - 4)(x + 2)}$

c) $\frac{37x}{42}$ **i)** $\frac{2x}{x^2 - y^2}$

d) $\frac{7x - 2y}{8}$ **j)** $\frac{2(a^2 + b^2)}{a^2 - b^2}$

e) $\frac{xyz + 4x + 4z}{4y}$ **k)** $\frac{7x^2 - 13x - 31}{(x + 5)(3x + 4)}$

f) $\frac{mn(pm + 1)}{p^2}$ **l)** $\frac{8x^2 + 10x + 11}{(2x - 3)(2x + 5)}$

Q8 **a)** $\frac{z}{15}$ **g)** $\frac{x^2 - 4x - 3}{x^2 - 9}$

b) $\frac{b(14 - a)}{7a}$ **h)** $\frac{y(x + 14)}{(x - 1)(x + 4)}$

c) $\frac{-3p - 4q}{4}$ **i)** $\frac{y^2 + 2y - 1}{2y^3}$

d) $-\frac{5}{6x}$ **j)** $\frac{2(x + 6)}{(3x - 4)(7x - 2)}$

e) $\frac{9x - 4y + xy}{3y}$ **k)** $\frac{10x + 29}{(4x - 1)(2x + 3)}$

f) $\frac{4a - 3a^2b + 8}{a^2(a + 2)}$ **l)** $\frac{x^2 + 13x + 19}{(x - 2)(x + 5)}$

Q9 **a)** $\frac{2x}{y}$ **d)** $\frac{2x + 5}{x - 4}$

b) $\frac{b + 2}{a^2 + b}$ **e)** $\frac{7(2x - 11)(x - 5)}{3}$

c) $\frac{1}{(x + 4)(x - 3)}$ **f)** $\frac{35(x + 2)}{2(2x + 1)}$

Q10 **a)** $\frac{3}{2xy^3}$ **d)** $\frac{7x(x + 1)}{2y(x - 4)}$

b) $4y^3$ **e)** $\frac{8(x + 6)}{3}$

c) $\frac{5}{3(2x + 1)}$ **f)** $2(x^2 - 4)$

Pages 31-32 — Sequences

Q1 **a)** 10, 12, 14; even numbers
b) 9, 11, 13; odd numbers
c) 25, 36, 49; square numbers
d) 125, 216, 343; cube numbers

Q2 **a)** 31, 36, 41   **b)** 5
c) $5n + 1$ **d)** 101

Q3 **a)** $2n$ **b)** $2n - 1$
c) $5n$ **d)** $3n + 2$

Q4 **a)** 19, 22, 25, $3n + 4$
b) 32, 37, 42, $5n + 7$
c) $-4, -14, -24, -10n + 46$
d) 47, 40, 33, $-7n + 82$

Q5 No. When $6n - 5 = 53$, n is
not a whole number.

Q6 **a)** $4n - 3$
b) 75 is not in the sequence because
when the expression for the nth term
is set to equal 75, n is not a whole
number.

Q7 **a)** $\frac{5}{11}, \frac{6}{13}, \frac{7}{15}$

b) $\frac{n}{2n + 1}$

Q8 **a)** $16\frac{7}{8}, 16\frac{9}{16}, 16\frac{23}{32}, 16\frac{41}{64}$
b) The 10th term will be the mean of the
8th and 9th terms.

Q9 **a)** Each term is the sum of the two
previous terms.
b) 39, 63, 102

Q10 **a)** 2, 10, 8
b) The sequence repeats every 6 terms.
c) 10

Q11 $u_2 = -1$, $u_3 = -4$

Q12 **a)** 80, 160, 320
b) 1296, 7776, 46 656
c) 25.6, 102.4, 409.6
d) 9, 3, 1   **g)** 63, 21, 7
e) 50, 10, 2   **h)** 9, $9\sqrt{3}$, 27
f) 48, 12, 3   **i)** 12, $12\sqrt{2}$, 24

Q13 **a)** arithmetic — common difference = 4
b) arithmetic — common difference = 10
c) geometric — common ratio = 3
d) arithmetic —
common difference = -1.2
e) geometric — common ratio = $\frac{1}{4}$
f) arithmetic —
common difference = -111

Q14 $(5n + 10) + (5(n + 1) + 10) = 145$
This gives $n = 12$, meaning the terms are
70 and 75.

Q15 **a)** 39, 53, 69   **d)** 93, 125, 161
$n^2 + 3n - 1$ $2n^2 + 10n - 7$
b) 18, 27, 38   **e)** 50, 71, 96
$n^2 - 2n + 3$ $2n^2 - n + 5$
c) 52, 68, 86   **f)** 93, 130, 173
$n^2 + 5n + 2$ $3n^2 + 4n - 2$

Q16 Setting $3n^2 - 5 = 43$ and solving gives
$n = 4$ so 43 is a term in the sequence.

Q17 **a)** 24, 35, 48 (the number of triangles
added increases by 2 each time).
b) $n(n + 2)$

Pages 33-35 — Inequalities

Q1 **a)** $9 \le x < 13$ **d)** $x < 5$
b) $-4 \le x < 1$ **e)** $x > 25$
c) $x \ge -4$ **f)** $-1 < x \le 3$

Q2 **a)** – **h)** (number lines)

Q3 **a)** $\{3, 4, 5, 6\}$ **b)** $\{-2, -1, 0, 1, 2\}$
c) $\{-5, -4, -3, -2, -1, 0\}$

Answers

Q4 **a)** $x > 3$ **i)** $x \geq 3$
b) $x < 4$ **j)** $x > 11$
c) $x \leq 5$ **k)** $x < 3$
d) $x \leq 6$ **l)** $x \geq -\frac{1}{2}$
e) $x \geq 7.5$ **m)** $x \leq -2$
f) $x < 4$ **n)** $x > 5$
g) $x < 7$ **o)** $x < 15$
h) $x < 4$ **p)** $x \geq -2$

Q5 **a)** $1 < x < 8$ **f)** $-1 < x < 23$
b) $0 \leq x \leq 8$ **g)** $-2 \leq x < 4$
c) $2 < x < 4$ **h)** $-51 < x \leq -11$
d) $-4 \leq x < -1$ **i)** $-16 < x \leq 5$
e) $5 \leq x \leq 10$

Q6 Largest integer for x is 2.

Q7 **a)** $x = 6$ **c)** $x = -1$
b) $x = 11$ **d)** $x = -7$

Q8 $\dfrac{11 - x}{2} < 5, x > 1$

Q9 **a)** $1130 \leq 32x$ **b)** 36

Q10 **a)** $900 \geq 18x$ **b)** 50

Q11 **a)** $x \geq 2, y > 1, x + y \leq 5$
b) $y \leq 2, x + y > 0, y \geq x + 2$

Q12

Q13

Q14 **a)** $x > 5, y \geq 7, x + y \geq 14$
b)

Q15 **a)** $-3 < x < 3$
b) $x < -4$ or $x > 4$
c) $-2 \leq x \leq 2$
d) $x \leq -3$ or $x \geq 3$
e) $x \leq -5$ or $x \geq 5$
f) $-4 < x < 4$
g) $x < -6$ or $x > 6$
h) $-2 < x < 2$
i) $x < -3$ or $x > 3$
j) $-7 \leq x \leq 7$
k) $x < -5$ or $x > 5$
l) $x < -6$ or $x > 6$

Q16 $y \geq x^2 - 1, y \geq \frac{1}{2}, x + y < 0$

Q17 **a)** $-2 < x < 3$
b) $-5 \leq x \leq -1$

c) $x < -2$ or $x > -1$
d) $x \leq 2$ or $x \geq 8$
e) $x < -2$ or $x > 9$
f) $-7 < x < -5$
g) $x \leq 4$ or $x \geq 5$
h) $-3 < x < 1$
i) $-2 \leq x \leq -\dfrac{3}{2}$
j) $x < \dfrac{1}{2}$ or $x > 4$
k) $-\dfrac{2}{3} < x < 1$
l) $x \leq -4$ or $x \geq \dfrac{5}{4}$

Page 36 — Iterative Methods

Q1

Guess (x)	Value of $x^3 + x^2 - 4x$	Too large/small
-3	$(-3)^3 + (-3)^2 - 4(-3) = -6$	Too small
-2	$(-2)^3 + (-2)^2 - 4(-2) = 4$	Too large
-2.1	$(-2.1)^3 + (-2.1)^2 - 4(-2.1) = 3.549$	Too large
-2.2	$(-2.2)^3 + (-2.2)^2 - 4(-2.2) = 2.99$	Too small
-2.15	$(-2.15)^3 + (-2.15)^2 - 4(-2.15) = 3.3$	Too large

So to 1 d.p. the solution is $x = -2.2$

Guess (x)	Value of $x^3 + x^2 - 4x$	Too large/small
-1	$-1 + 1 + 4 = 4$	Too large
0	$0 + 0 - 0 = 0$	Too small
-0.8	$(-0.8)^3 + (-0.8)^2 - 4(-0.8) = 3.328$	Too large
-0.7	$(-0.7)^3 + (-0.7)^2 - 4(-0.7) = 2.947$	Too small
-0.75	$(-0.75)^3 + (-0.75)^2 - 4(-0.75) = 3.141$	Too large

So to 1 d.p. the solution is $x = -0.7$

Guess (x)	Value of $x^3 + x^2 - 4x$	Too large/small
1	$1 + 1 - 4 = -2$	Too small
2	$8 + 4 - 8 = 4$	Too large
1.9	$(1.9)^3 + (1.9)^2 - 4(1.9) = 2.869$	Too small
1.95	$(1.95)^3 + (1.95)^2 - 4(1.95) = 3.417$	Too large

So to 1 d.p. the solution is $x = 1.9$

Q2

x	Value of $x^3 - 8x^2 - 3x + 9$	Positive/Negative
-2.0	-25	Negative
-1.9	-21.039	Negative
-1.8	-17.352	Negative
-1.7	-13.933	Negative
-1.6	-10.776	Negative
-1.5	-7.875	Negative
-1.4	-5.224	Negative
-1.3	-2.817	Negative
-1.2	-0.648	Negative
-1.1	1.289	Positive

x	Value of $x^3 - 8x^2 - 3x + 9$	Positive/Negative
-1.19	-0.443959	Negative
-1.18	-0.242232	Negative
-1.17	-0.042813	Negative
-1.16	0.154304	Positive

The solution between -2 and -1 is -1.2 to 1 d.p.

x	Value of $x^3 - 8x^2 - 3x + 9$	Positive/Negative
0.0	9	Positive
0.1	8.621	Positive
0.2	8.088	Positive
0.3	7.407	Positive
0.4	6.584	Positive
0.5	5.625	Positive
0.6	4.536	Positive
0.7	3.323	Positive
0.8	1.992	Positive
0.9	0.549	Positive
1.0	-1	Negative

x	Value of $x^3 - 8x^2 - 3x + 9$	Positive/Negative
0.91	0.398771	Positive
0.92	0.247488	Positive
0.93	0.095157	Positive
0.94	-0.058216	Negative

The solution between 0 and 1 is 0.9 to 1 d.p.

x	Value of $x^3 - 8x^2 - 3x + 9$	Positive/Negative
8.0	-15	Negative
8.1	-8.739	Negative
8.2	-2.152	Negative
8.3	4.767	Positive

x	Value of $x^3 - 8x^2 - 3x + 9$	Positive/Negative
8.21	-1.475139	Negative
8.22	-0.794952	Negative
8.23	-0.111433	Negative
8.24	0.575424	Positive

The solution between 8 and 9 is 8.2 to 1 d.p.

Q3 $x_0 = 3$
$x_1 = 3.1072... \neq x_0$ to 2 d.p.
$x_2 = 3.1442... \neq x_1$ to 2 d.p.
$x_3 = 3.1569... \neq x_2$ to 2 d.p.
$x_4 = 3.1613... = x_3$ to 2 d.p.
The solution is 3.16 to 2 d.p.

Q4 **a)** $x_0 = 0$
$x_1 = 0.2 \neq x_0$ to 3 d.p.
$x_2 = 0.20336... \neq x_1$ to 3 d.p.
$x_3 = 0.20336... = x_2$ to 3 d.p.
The solution is 0.203 to 3 d.p.
b) $x_0 = -2$
$x_1 = -1.73684... \neq x_0$ to 3 d.p.
$x_2 = -1.67618... \neq x_1$ to 3 d.p.
$x_3 = -1.67299... \neq x_2$ to 3 d.p.
$x_4 = -1.67298... = x_3$ to 3 d.p.
The solution is -1.673 to 3 d.p.
c) $x_0 = 2$
$x_1 = 1.63157... \neq x_0$ to 3 d.p.
$x_2 = 1.49224... \neq x_1$ to 3 d.p.
$x_3 = 1.47016... \neq x_2$ to 3 d.p.
$x_4 = 1.46961... = x_3$ to 3 d.p.
The solution is 1.470 to 3 d.p.

Page 37 — Simultaneous Equations

Q1 **a)** $x = 1, y = 2$
b) $x = -1\frac{1}{2}, y = 4$
c) $x = 1, y = 9$
d) $x = 8, y = -\dfrac{1}{2}$
e) $x = 1, y = 3$

f) $x = 2, y = 1$
g) $x = 3, y = 5$
h) $x = \frac{1}{2}, y = 2$
i) $x = 5, y = 9$

Q2 **a)** $x = 4, y = 18$ OR $x = -3, y = 11$

b) $x = 6, y = 28$ OR $x = -3, y = 1$

c) $x = 1.5, y = 4.5$ OR $x = -1, y = 2$

d) $x = 5, y = 23$ OR $x = -2, y = 2$

e) $x = \frac{1}{3}, y = -\frac{29}{3}$ OR $x = 4, y = 38$

f) $x = \frac{1}{2}, y = -\frac{3}{2}$ OR $x = -2, y = 6$

g) $x = -3, y = \frac{33}{5}$ OR $x = 2, y = \frac{28}{5}$

h) $x = -\frac{1}{4}, y = \frac{17}{4}$ OR $x = -3, y = 40$

i) $x = -\frac{2}{3}, y = \frac{31}{3}$ OR $x = -4, y = 57$

j) $x = -3, y = -2$ OR $x = 2, y = 3$

k) $x = -3, y = 3$

l) $x = 2, y = 3$ OR $x = -\frac{2}{3}, y = -\frac{7}{3}$

Q3 **a)** $6x + 5y = 430$
$4x + 10y = 500$
b) $x = 45, y = 32$

Q4 7 chickens
4 cats

Q5 $3y + 2x = 18$
$y + 3x = 6$ $x = 0, y = 6$
$4y + 5x = 7$
$2x - 3y = 12$ $x = 3, y = -2$
$4x - 6y = 13$
$x + y = 2$ $x = 2\frac{1}{2}, y = -\frac{1}{2}$

Q6 $5m + 2c = 344$
$4m + 3c = 397$
$m = 34, c = 87$

Q7 $x = 12, y = 2$

Q8 $(3, 2)$ and $(-1, 6)$

Pages 38-39 — Proof

Q1 $(n + 3)^2 - (3n + 5)$
$= (n + 3)(n + 3) - (3n + 5)$
$= n^2 + 6n + 9 - 3n - 5$
$= n^2 + 3n + 2 + 2$
$= (n + 1)(n + 2) + 2$

Q2 $(n - 3)^2 - (n - 5)$
$= (n - 3)(n - 3) - (n - 5)$
$= n^2 - 6n + 9 - n + 5$
$= n^2 - 7n + 12 + 2$
$= (n - 3)(n - 4) + 2$

Q3 $25 - \frac{(x - 8)^2}{4}$
$= \frac{100 - (x - 8)^2}{4}$
$= \frac{-x^2 + 16x + 36}{4}$
$= \frac{(2 + x)(18 - x)}{4}$

Q4 Collecting like terms on the LHS gives
$(3a - 2)x + 21 - 2b$. So equating the x
coefficients gives $3a - 2 = 4$, so $a = 2$.
Equating the constants gives
$21 - 2b = 29$, so $b = -4$.

Q5 $(2n + 1)^2 - (2n - 1)^2 - 10$
$= (4n^2 + 4n + 1) - (4n^2 - 4n + 1) - 10$
$= 8n - 10$
Dividing this by 8 gives $n - \frac{5}{4}$
(not a whole number), so the expression
is not a multiple of 8.

Q6 $n + (n + 1) + (n + 2)$
$= 3n + 3 = 3(n + 1)$
Dividing this by 3 gives $n + 1$ (a whole
number), so the sum is divisible by 3.

Q7 $2a \times 2b = 4ab = 2 \times 2ab$. This is
divisible by 2 and so is even.

Q8 $2n + (2n + 2) + (2n + 4)$
$= 6n + 6 = 6(n + 1)$
Dividing this by 6 gives $n + 1$ (a whole
number), so the sum is a multiple of 6.

Q9 **a)** $(2n + 1) + (2n + 3)$
$= 4n + 4 = 4(n + 1)$
Dividing this by 4 gives $n + 1$
(a whole number), so the sum is a
multiple of 4.
b) $(2n + 1)^2 + (2n + 3)^2$
$= 4n^2 + 4n + 1 + 4n^2 + 12n + 9$
$= 8n^2 + 16n + 10$
Dividing this by 4 gives $2n^2 + 4n + \frac{5}{2}$
(not a whole number), so the sum is
not a multiple of 4.

Q10 2 is a prime number as it only divides
by 1 and itself. 2 is even so Maisy is
wrong.

Q11 **a)** E.g. 3 and 1 are both odd numbers
but if you add them together you get
4, which is even so the statement is
wrong.
b) E.g. If $n = 6$, $n^2 = 36$, which is
divisible by 4, but 6 is not divisible by
4, so the statement is wrong.

Q12 E.g. If $a = 1$ and $b = -1$, then
$a^2 = 1$ and $b^2 = 1$. So $a^2 = b^2$ but a does
not equal b, so the statement is wrong.

Q13 $5^{20} - 5^{19}$
$= 5 \times 5^{19} - 5^{19}$
$= 5^{19}(5 - 1) = 4 \times 5^{19}$
$= 2 \times 2 \times 5^{19}$
$= 2n$ where $n = 2 \times 5^{19}$
So $5^{20} - 5^{19}$ is even.

Q14 $21^8 + 15^4$
$= 21 \times 21^7 + 15 \times 15^3$
$= (3 \times 7 \times 21^7) + (3 \times 5 \times 15^3)$
$= 3[(7 \times 21^7) + (5 \times 15^3)]$
$= 3x$ where $x = (7 \times 21^7) + (5 \times 15^3)$
So $21^8 + 15^4$ is a multiple of 3.

Q15 $3^8 - 1$ can be factorised to
$(3^4 - 1)(3^4 + 1)$, so it has factors that are
not equal to itself or 1. Therefore, it is
not a prime number.

Q16 $\frac{1}{2}n^2 - \frac{5}{2}n + 3$
$+ \frac{1}{2}(n + 1)^2 - \frac{5}{2}(n + 1) + 3$
$= n^2 - 4n + 4$
$= (n - 2)^2$ which is a square number.

Q17 $b = 5^{72} \times 4^{38} = 5^{72} \times (2^2)^{38} = 5^{72} \times 2^{76}$
So $ab = 5^{99} \times 2^{98} \times 5^{72} \times 2^{76}$
$= 5^{99 + 72} \times 2^{98 + 76}$
$= 5^{171} \times 2^{174} = 5^{171} \times 2^{171} \times 2^3$
$= 2^3 \times 10^{171} = 8 \times 10^{171}$,
which has 172 digits.

Q18 $\frac{y^2 + 1}{y^2} - \frac{x^2 + 1}{x^2} = \frac{x^2 - y^2}{(xy)^2}$
$x^2 - y^2 < 0$ since $x > 0, y > 0$ and $x < y$.
Also, $(xy)^2$ is always positive.
Therefore, $\frac{x^2 - y^2}{(xy)^2} < 0$
which means $\frac{y^2 + 1}{y^2} - \frac{x^2 + 1}{x^2} < 0$

Q19 Call the sum of the numbers in the set n.
Then the mean of the set is $\frac{n}{6} = 18$.
The sum of the numbers in the new set
will be $n - 6$, so the mean of the new set
will be $\frac{n - 6}{6} = \frac{n}{6} - \frac{6}{6} = 18 - 1 = 17$.

Q20 $n^2 - 2n + 2 + (n + 1)^2 - 2(n + 1) + 2$
$= n^2 - 2n + 2 + n^2 + 2n + 1 - 2n - 2 + 2$
$= 2n^2 - 2n + 3$
$= 2n^2 - 2n + 2 + 1$
$= 2(n^2 - n + 1) + 1$
$= 2x + 1$ where $x = (n^2 - n + 1)$
So the sum of two consecutive terms is
an odd number.

Q21 If $x^2 + 3 > 2x + 1$,
then $x^2 - 2x + 2 > 0$
and $(x - 1)^2 + 1 > 0$
This is always true as $(x - 1)^2$ cannot be
negative. So the inequality always holds
and Fay is correct.

Page 40 — Functions

Q1 $f(x) = 2(x - 4)$ or $2x - 8$

Q2 **a)** $x = 4.5$ **d)** $x = \pm 1$
b) $x = 0.75$ **e)** $x = 0.27$ or -7.27
c) $x = 4$ **f)** $x = 5$

Q3 **a)** $f(5) = 9$ **d)** $f(5) = 13$
b) $f(5) = 30$ **e)** $f(5) = 0.484$
c) $f(5) = 38$ **f)** $f(5) = 520$

Q4 **a)** $f(8) = 44$
b) $g(3) = -6$
c) $f(x) + g(x) = 15 + 4x - x^2$
d) $f(2) - g(2) = 21$
e) $f(-4) = -4$
f) $gf(x) = -16x^2 - 96x - 141$
g) $fg(x) = 24 - 4x^2$
h) $gf(2) = -397$

Q5 **a)** $f(-1) = 8$
b) $g(1/3) = 27$
c) $hf(x) = 4x^2 - 24x + 42$
d) $gf(x) = 9 \div (6 - 2x)$
e) $fg(12) = 4.5$
f) $hf(-9) = 582$

Q6 **a)** $h^{-1}(x) = x - 6$
b) $f^{-1}(x) = \frac{11}{x} - 1$
c) $h^{-1}(x) + f^{-1}(x) = x - 7 + \frac{11}{x}$
d) $f^{-1}(11) - h^{-1}(6) = 0$
e) $g^{-1}(h(x)) = \frac{4}{3}(6 + x)$
f) $f^{-1}(g(x)) = \frac{44}{3x} - 1$
g) $h^{-1}(f(5)) = -4.1\dot{6}$
h) $h^{-1}(g(-1)) = -6.75$

Q7 **a)** $f(-1) = -0.67$
b) $g(9) = 554$
c) $kj(-3) = 210$
d) $n^{-1}(2) = 14.5$

e) $t^{-1}(3) = -39$
f) $v^{-1}(r(2)) = -16$

Q8 **a)** $fg(x) = 2(7 - x)^3$

b) $m^{-1}(x) = \dfrac{5x + 6}{9}$

c) $p^{-1}(q(x)) = \dfrac{\left(\frac{13}{x-2}\right) - 5}{8} = \dfrac{23 - 5x}{8x - 16}$

Q9 $f(x) = 3(x + 11) - 6 = 3x + 27$
If output is greater than input:
$3x + 27 > x$
$2x > -27$
$x > -13.5$

Section Three — Graphs

Page 41 — Straight Lines and Gradients

Q1 **a)** B   **f)** F
b) A   **g)** C
c) F   **h)** B
d) G   **i)** D
e) E   **j)** H

Q2 **a)** $-\dfrac{1}{2}$ **f)** $-\dfrac{8}{3}$

b) 3   **g)** 4

c) $-\dfrac{1}{4}$ **h)** 1

d) -2   **i)** -1

e) $-\dfrac{2}{3}$ **j)** $\dfrac{1}{3}$

Q3 **a)** 2   **d)** -2

b) $\dfrac{1}{2}$ **e)** $\dfrac{1}{2}$

c) -1   **f)** $-\dfrac{3}{4}$

Q4 $a = 5, b = 0$

Page 42 — y = mx + c

Q1 **a)** m = 4, (0, 3)
b) m = 3, (0, -2)
c) m = 2, (0, 1)
d) m = -3, (0, 3)
e) m = 5, (0, 0)
f) m = -2, (0, 3)
g) m = -6, (0, -4)
h) m = 1, (0, 0)
i) m = $-\dfrac{1}{2}$, (0, 3)

j) m = $\dfrac{1}{4}$, (0, 2)

k) m = $\dfrac{4}{3}$, (0, 2)

Q2 **a)** $y = \dfrac{7}{2}x - 1$ **d)** $y = \dfrac{1}{4}x - 3$

b) $y = \dfrac{1}{2}x + 4$ **e)** $y = -\dfrac{1}{2}x$

c) $y = -\dfrac{1}{5}x + 7$ **f)** $y = -2x - 6$

Q3 **a)** $y = x + 4$ **c)** $y = -x$
b) $y = 3x + 2$ **d)** $y = -3x + 4$

Q4 **a)** $y = x$ **c)** $y = -3x + 3$
b) $y = 3x$ **d)** $y = -2x - 4$

Q5 **a)** $a = 4$ **c)** $c = 7$
b) $b = 8$ **d)** $d = 9$

Q6 (7, 20) and (5, 14)

Page 43 — Drawing Straight Line Graphs

Q1

x	0	3	8
y	3	9	19

a) 13   **c)** 4
b) 7   **d)** 7

Q2

x	-8	-4	8
y	-5	-4	-1

a) -2.5   **c)** 4
b) -3   **d)** 6

Q3 **a)** m = 3, c = 1

b) m = $\dfrac{1}{2}$, c = -5

c) m = -3, c = 4
d) m = -1, c = -1

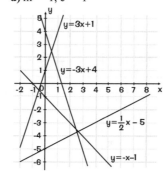

Q4 **a)** $y = \dfrac{2}{3}x - \dfrac{8}{3}$

b) $\left(0, -\dfrac{8}{3}\right)$

c) m = $\dfrac{2}{3}$

d)

Q5

a)

b)

c)

d)

e)

f)

Page 44 — Coordinates and Ratio

Q1 **a)** (3, 4)   **d)** (3, 3.5)
b) (5.5, 11)   **e)** (9.5, 9.5)
c) (8.5, 9)   **f)** (30.5, 20.5)

Q2 (110, 135)

Q3 **a)** (2, 5.5)   **d)** (2, 3)
b) (0.5, 1.5)   **e)** (–13, –12.5)
c) (2, –2.5)

Q4 **a)** Q = (4, 6)   **d)** Q = (-15, -15)
b) Q = (8, 11)   **e)** Q = (17.5, -7.25)
c) Q = (4.5, 0)   **f)** Q = (-8, -6.375)

Q5 C = (-22, -10.5)

Q6 **a)** (2.5, 3)
b) Yes — since FH is a diameter, its midpoint is the centre of the circle. The midpoint of FH is (2.5, 3), which is point G.

Page 45 — Parallel and Perpendicular Lines

Q1 **a)** parallel   **e)** neither
b) parallel   **f)** perpendicular
c) neither   **g)** parallel
d) perpendicular   **h)** perpendicular

Q2 **a)** m = 3
b) $y = 3x + 1$

Q3 **a)** m = -2
b) $y = -2x - 3$

Q4 **a)** $y = 2x + 3$ **e)** $y = 2x + 13$

b) $y = 4x + 1$ **f)** $y = \dfrac{1}{8}x + \dfrac{1}{8}$

c) $y = x - 8$ **g)** $y = \dfrac{1}{2}x + 39$

d) $y = -\dfrac{2}{3}x + 6$ **h)** $y = -\dfrac{8}{3}x - 5$

Q5 **a)** $y = -\dfrac{1}{2}x + 3$

b) $y = -\dfrac{1}{3}x + 1$

c) $y = x - 6$

Page 46 — Quadratic Graphs

Q1

x	-4	-3	-2	-1	0	1	2	3	4
$y = 2x^2$	32	18	8	2	0	2	8	18	32

Q6

Intersection at (2, 2)

Q2

x	-4	-3	-2	-1	0	1	2	3
x^2	16	9	4	1	0	1	4	9
3x	-12	-9	-6	-3	0	3	6	9
$y=x^2+3x+5$	9	5	3	3	5	9	15	23

Line of symmetry x = –1.5

$y = x^2 + 3x + 5$

Q3

x	-4	-3	-2	-1	0	1	2	3	4
$-x^2$	-16	-9	-4	-1	0	-1	-4	-9	-16
$y=3-x^2$	-13	-6	-1	2	3	2	-1	-6	-13

a)

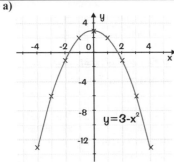

$y=3-x^2$

b) 3

Q4 **a)** c = -8 **c)** -4 and 1
b) (-1.5, -12.5)

Q5 **a)**

$y=x^2+8x-20$

(-4, -36)

b)

$y=x^2-5x+6$

(2.5, -0.25)

c)

(0, 1)

$y=-x^2+1$

d)

$y=-x^2-4x-4$

Pages 47-50 — Harder Graphs

Q1 **a)** (v)   **g)** (xii)
b) (vii)   **h)** (iv)
c) (vi)   **i)** (ix)
d) (x)   **j)** (ii)
e) (xi)   **k)** (iii)
f) (viii)   **l)** (i)

Q2

x	-3	-2	-1	0	1	2	3
x^3	-27	-8	-1	0	1	8	27
+4	4	4	4	4	4	4	4
y	-23	-4	3	4	5	12	31

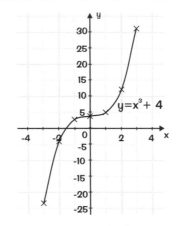

$y=x^3+4$

Q3

x	-3	-2	-1	0	1	2	3
$-x^3$	27	8	1	0	-1	-8	-27
-4	-4	-4	-4	-4	-4	-4	-4
y	23	4	-3	-4	-5	-12	-31

$y=-x^3-4$

Q4

$y=2x^3+3x-6$

Q5

$y=x^3+2x^2-5x$

Q6 **a)** and **b)**

$x^2+y^2=49$

$x^2+y^2=4$

Q7 **a)** $x^2+y^2=9$
b) $x^2+y^2=144$
c) $x^2+y^2=36$

Q8 radius = 5
$x^2+y^2=25$

Q9 radius = 17
$x^2+y^2=289$

Q10 **a)** $y=-\dfrac{5}{12}x+\dfrac{169}{12}$

b) $y=\dfrac{12}{5}x-\dfrac{169}{5}$

c) $y=-\dfrac{12}{5}x-\dfrac{169}{5}$

a) and **b)** are perpendicular.

Q11

x	-4	-3	-2	-1	0	1	2	3	4
$y=1/x$	-0.25	-0.33	-0.5	-1	n/a	1	0.5	0.33	0.25

$y = 1/x$

Q12 **a)**

x	-4	-3	-2	-1	0	1	2	3	4
$y=2^x$	0.06	0.1	0.3	0.5	1	2	4	8	16

b)

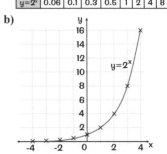

$y=2^x$

c) Anything to the power of 0 is 1.

Q13

x	-3	-2	-1	0	1	2	3
3^x	0.04	0.1	0.3	1	3	9	27
6/x	-2	-3	-6	n/a	6	3	2
$y=3^x-6/x$	2.04	3.1	6.3		-3	6	25

Q14 a) to c)

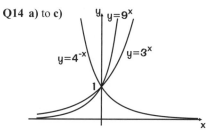

Q15 a) $a = 12$, $b = 3$
b) $S = 12 \times 3^5$
= 2916

Q16 A(180°, 0), B(90°, 1), C(–90°, –1)

Q17 D(270°, 0)
E(90°, 0)
F(0°, 1)
G(–90°, 0)

Q18 A $y = \sin x$ F $y = \sin x$
B $y = \cos x$ G $y = \cos x$
C $y = \cos x$ H $y = \sin x$
D $y = \sin x$ I $y = \cos x$
E $y = \sin x$

Q19

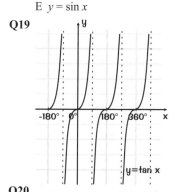

Q20

x	0°	90°	180°	270°	360°
y	2	1	0	1	2

Page 51 — Solving Equations Using Graphs

Q1 **a)** $x = 3$, $y = 3$ **f)** $x = 1$, $y = 2$
b) $x = 2$, $y = 5$ **g)** $x = 2$, $y = 3$
c) $x = 1$, $y = 2$ **h)** $x = 2$, $y = 3$
d) $x = 1$, $y = 2$ **i)** $x = 5$, $y = 2$
e) $x = 1$, $y = 4$ **j)** $x = 3$, $y = 4$

Q2 **a)** $x = 0.7$, $y = 2.7$
b) $x = 1.6$, $y = 0.9$
and $x = -2.6$, $y = 9.1$

Q3 **a)** $x = 0$, $x = 1$
b) $x = 2.7$, $x = -0.7$
c) $x = 3.4$, $x = -2.4$

Q4

x	-4	-3	-2	-1	0	1	2	3	4
-½x²	-8	-4.5	-2	-0.5	0	-0.5	-2	-4.5	-8
+5	5	5	5	5	5	5	5	5	5
y	-3	0.5	3	4.5	5	4.5	3	0.5	-3

a) i) $x = 3.2$, $x = -3.2$ (allow ±0.1)
ii) $x = 4$, $x = -4$
iii) $x = 2.3$, $x = -4.3$ (allow ±0.1)
b) $y = 2x + 2$

Pages 52-53 — Graph Transformations

Q1 a) to d)

e) and f)

Q2 a) to d)

e) and f)

g) and h)

Q3 Graph is reflected in the x-axis and the y-axis.

Q4 a)

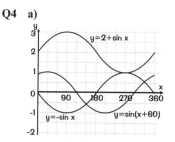

b) (0, 0), (180, 0), (360, 0)

Q5 a) and b)

Q6 a) $(4, \frac{3}{2})$ **d)** $(0, 0)$

b) $(1, \frac{7}{2})$ **e)** $(-1, \frac{3}{2})$

c) $(1, -\frac{3}{2})$ **f)** $(\frac{4}{3}, \frac{11}{2})$

Q7 $y = -x^3 - 2x + 4$

Page 54 — Real-Life Graphs

Q1 1D, 2B, 3A, 4E, 5C

Q2 a)

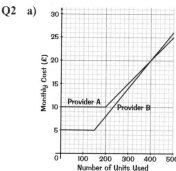

b) i) Provider A: £12.50
Provider B: £11
ii) Provider A: £24
Provider B: £24.80 (accept £25)
c) 400 units

Page 55 — Distance-Time Graphs

Q1 a) 85 mins
b) 80 mins
c) 16.9 mph (to 1 d.p.)
d) 57.6 mph
e) No, because the total driving time is 80 minutes.

Q2 a) B   **b)** 3¾ mins
c) B
d) i) 267 m/min (to 3 s.f.)
ii) 16.0 km/h (to 3 s.f.)
e) C was the fastest;
700 m/min or 42 km/h

Q3 a) 3.33 m/s
b) 3.6 m/s (accept between 3.3 m/s and 4 m/s)

c)

d) Gabrielle — it takes 100 s for Gabrielle to cycle 500 m and 150 s for Richard.

Page 56 — Velocity-Time Graphs

Q1 a) 100 km/h
b) 2 hours
c) 100 km/h²

Q2 a) i) 17.5 km   **ii)** 50 km
b) 102.5 km

Q3 a)

Distance ≈
$(\frac{1}{2} \times 20 \times 56) + (20 \times 56)$
$+ (\frac{1}{2} \times (56 + 104) \times 20) + (20 \times 104)$
= 5360 m

(Answers will depend on how you've divided the area into chunks.)
b) Accept between 4 m/s² and 6 m/s²

Page 57 — Gradients of Real-Life Graphs

Q1 a) 4 earwigs per day
b) Days 8-12
c) 3 earwigs per day

Q2 a) 6.5 °C per hour (accept between 5.5 °C per hour and 7.5 °C per hour)
b) 5.67 °C per hour

Q3 a) 1.6 cm per minute (graph is steepest at 8 minutes, accept between 1.4 cm per minute and 1.8 cm per minute)
b) -1.5 cm per minute

Section Four — Ratio, Proportion and Rates of Change

Pages 58-60 — Ratios

Q1 a) i) There are $\frac{2}{5}$ as many cats as dogs.
ii) There are $\frac{5}{2}$ times as many dogs as cats.
b) i) There are $\frac{3}{4}$ as many sprouts as peas.
ii) There are $\frac{4}{3}$ times as many peas as sprouts.

Q2 a) 3:4   **f)** 9:1
b) 1:4   **g)** 30:1
c) 1:2   **h)** 8:5
d) 9:16   **i)** 1:3
e) 7:2

Q3 a) 6 cm   **d)** 1.5 cm
b) 11 cm   **e)** 2.75 cm
c) 30.4 m   **f)** 7.6 m

Q4 a) £8, £12
b) 80 m, 70 m
c) 100 g, 200 g, 200 g.
d) 1hr 20 m, 2 hr 40 m, 4 hrs.

Q5 John 4, Peter 12

Q6 400 ml, 600 ml, 1000 ml

Q7 30

Q8 Jane £40, Holly £48, Rosemary £12

Q9 Sunil got £12, Paul got £16

Q10 a) 250/500 = 1/2 **b)** 150/500 = 3/10

Q11 a) 245 girls   **b)** 210 boys

Q12 a) £39   **b)** £140

Q13 a) 1:300   **b)** 6 m   **c)** 3.3 cm

Q14 a) i) 15 kg   **ii)** 30 kg
b) 8 kg cement, 24 kg sand and 48 kg gravel.

Q15 a) i) 30 fine   **ii)** 15 not fine
b) 30/45 = 2/3

Q16 a) 45 Salt & Vinegar
b) 90 bags sold altogether

Q17 a) 1:9   **b)** 1:0.625
c) 1:8.6̇   **d)** 1:2.083̇

Q18 3:8

Q19 2:3

Q20 3:4

Q21 60% of 70% + 20% of 30%
= 0.6 × 70% + 0.2 × 30%
= 42% + 6% = 48%

Q22 $(a + 1) : (b - 8) = 4 : 1$
and $(a + 5) : (b - 10) = 10 : 1$
These give the simultaneous equations
$a + 1 = 4b - 32$ and $a + 5 = 10b - 100$
Solve to give $a = 15$ and $b = 12$.
So the jacket originally cost £15 and the gloves £12.

Q23 a) $\frac{5}{7}$ **b)** 2:5
c) Call the number of spotted hats x and the number of striped hats y.
Then $x : y = 2 : 5$ and $x : (y - 5) = 1 : 2$.
These give the simultaneous equations $5x = 2y$ and $2x = y - 5$.
Solve to give $x = 10$ and $y = 25$.
So Jack has 10 spotted hats.

Q24 Call the number of apples a and the number of bananas b.
Then $b : (a + b) = 2 : 5$ and $(b - 3) : (a + b - 3) = 1 : 4$.
These give the simultaneous equations $3b - 2a = 0$ and $3b - a = 9$.
Solve to give $a = 9$ and $b = 6$.
So there were originally 9 apples and 6 bananas in the bowl.

Pages 61-62 — Direct and Inverse Proportion

Q1 a) 400 g

b) 300 g
c) She doesn't have enough as she will need 350 g of butter.

Q2 53.77 Pentagonia dollars

Q3 E.g.

Q4 £510

Q5 25 g

Q6 a) 4 hours
b) 6 hours 12 minutes
c) 2 hours 4 minutes

Q7 a) 4 postal workers
b) E.g. If some postal workers worked at a slower rate, more workers might be needed.

Q8 a) 30 bikes   **b)** 32 bikes

Q9 a) $y = \frac{1}{5}x$ **b)** $y = 20$

Q10 a) $y = 184.8$
b) E.g.

Q11 a) $y = \frac{24}{x}$
b) $y = 2$

Q12 a) $x = 2$
b) E.g.

Q13

x	1	2	3	4	5	6
y	48	24	16	12	9.6	8

Q14 a)

x	1	2	5	10
y	100	25	4	1

b)

x	2	4	6	8
y	24	6	2²/₃	1.5

Q15 4 kg

Q16 a) $r = 19.2$ **b)** $s = 2$
c) $r = -37.5$ **d)** $s = -20$

Q17 9.5 N/kg

Pages 63-65 — Percentages

Q1 a) £1.28
b) 629 kg
c) 16 mins

Q2 72.5%

Q3 a) £4275   **b)** £6840

Q4 1.6%

Q5 500%

Q6 25%

Q7 32%

Q8 £358.80

Q9 £244.40

Q10 23 300 (to 3 s.f.)

Q11 Car 1 costs £8495 × (1 − 0.15) = £7220.75.
Car 2 costs £8195 × (1 − 0.12) = £7211.60.
So car 2 is the cheapest.

Q12 £5980

Q13 £152.75, so no, he couldn't afford it.

Q14 a) £284.25
b) £276

Q15 31%

Q16 13%

Q17 a) 67.7% **b)** 93.5%
c) 38.1%

Q18 60%

Q19 23%

Q20 £80

Q21 a) 300 **b)** 4 whole years

Q22 a) £2.50 **b)** £1.60

Q23 15%

Q24 38%

Q25 Original area = $0.5ab$

New area = $\dfrac{1.33a \times 0.88b}{2} = 0.5852ab$

% change = $\dfrac{0.5852ab - 0.5ab}{0.5ab} \times 100$

= 17.04% increase

Q26 53%

Pages 66-67 — Compound Growth and Decay

Q1 a) £473.47 **c)** £909.12
b) £612.52 **d)** £1081.90

Q2 a) 281 **c)** 27 hours
b) 3036

Q3 a) 8.214 kg **c)** 7.272 kg
b) 7.497 kg **d)** 3.836 kg

Q4 a) £1920.80 **c)** £434.06
b) £27 671.04 **d)** £34 974.86

Q5 Second option by £2.21

Q6 £3200 (to the nearest £100)

Q7 a) 910.91 **c)** 114.39
b) 754.32 **d)** about 30 hours

Q8 a) £9980.90
b) £7877.94
c) £27 116.06

Q9 a) 5060 **c)** 5045
b) 5173 **d)** 6056

Q10 a) £100 000
b) From 2012-2015 the prices are £100 000, £120 000, £144 000, £172 800. This is a sequence with a common ratio of 1.2 so they form a geometric progression.

Q11 £220.44

Q12 a) 16.85 million
b) 20.72 million
c) 14.81 million

Pages 68-69 — Unit Conversions

Q1 1400 cm³

Q2 a) 33 mm **g)** 0.007 kg
b) 0.06 kg **h)** 0.95 kg
c) 48 in **i)** 72 in

d) 3 ft **j)** 80 oz
e) 7 ft 3 in **k)** 100 yd 1 ft
f) 2 lb 11 oz **l)** 0.0006 m

Q3 147 kg × 2.2 = 323.4 lbs

Q4 14 gallons = 14 × 4.5 = 63 litres

Q5 9 stone 4 lbs = 130 lbs
130 lbs ÷ 2.2 = 59.1 kg

Q6 Barry cycled 30 miles = 30 × 1.6 = 48 km. So Barbara cycled furthest.

Q7 a) 18 in = 1.5 feet ≈ 45 cm
b) 450 mm

Q8 a) 21 feet = 21 × 12 = 252 in
b) 21 feet = 21 ÷ 3 = 7 yd
c) 21 feet = 21 × 30 = 630 cm
d) 630 cm = 630 ÷ 100 000 = 0.0063 km

Q9 a) 60 kg = 60 × 2.2 = 132 lbs
b) 132 lbs = 132 × 16 = 2112 oz
c) 10 st. = 140 lbs, so Sylvester can lift most.

Q10 5 lb = 5 ÷ 2.2 = 2.3 kg. So Dick needs to buy 3 bags of sugar.

Q11 a) £52
b) £35 = €42, so he does have enough money.
c) From the graph, €15 = £12.50. 1 kg ≈ 2.2 lbs, so steak costs 12.50 ÷ 2.2 ≈ £5.68 per 1b.

Q12 a) 40 × 1.6 = 64 km/h
b) 18.8 × 3600 = 67 680 m/h
67 680 ÷ 1000 = 67.68 km/h
67.68 − 64 = 3.68 km/h, so the car was 3.68 km/h over the speed limit.
c) 1750 × 3600 = 6 300 000 cm/h
6 300 000 ÷ 100 000 = 63 km/h
64 − 63 = 1, so the car was 1 km/h under the speed limit.

Q13 a) 900 ÷ 100 = 9 cm²
b) 15 × 1 000 000 = 15 000 000 mm²
c) 4 × 10 000 = 40 000 cm²
d) 500 ÷ 10 000 = 0.05 m²
e) 38 × 100 = 3800 mm²
f) 860 000 ÷ 1 000 000 = 0.86 m²

Q14 a) 2500 × 1 000 000 = 2 500 000 000 cm³
b) 2500 × 1 000 000 000 = 2 500 000 000 000 mm³

Q15 682 000 ÷ 1000 = 682 cm³
The volume of the brain is bigger than the volume of the skull so the scientist can't be right.

Q16 840 cm³ = 840 ÷ 100³ = 0.00084 m³
2058 g = 2.058 kg
Density = 2.058 ÷ 0.00084 = 2450 kg/m³

Q17 10 miles ≈ 16 km
Matt drinks 135 × 16 = 2160 ml
= 2.16 litres ≈ 2.16 ÷ 4.5 = 0.48 gallons
This costs 0.48 × 95 = 45.6 p
= 46 p (to the nearest penny)

Pages 70-72 — Speed, Density and Pressure

Q1 a) 100/11 = 9.09 m/s (to 2 d.p)
b) 32.73 km/h

Q2 7 minutes to go 63 miles so 540 mph

Q3 $\dfrac{260}{71}$ hours = 3.66 hrs ≈ 3 hrs 40 min
07.05 to 10.30 is 3 hrs 25 mins.
Journey takes over 3 hrs 25 mins, so no.

Q4 a) 98.9 mph (to 3 s.f.)
b) 99.2 mph (to 3 s.f.)

Q5 a) 2.77 + 1.96 + 0.6 = 5.33 hrs (to 3 s.f.) = 5 hours 20 mins
b) 46.9 mph (to 3 s.f.)

Q6 2.15pm

Q7 a) 2.23 hrs (2 hrs 14 mins)
b) 1 hr 49 mins + 10 mins = 1 hr 59 mins
c) 1346 and 1401

Q8 The first athlete ran at 16000 ÷ (60 × 60) = 4.44 m/s, so was faster than the second athlete (at 4 m/s). The first athlete would take 37.5 mins to run 10 km; the second would take 41.7 mins.

Q9 a) 487.5 km
b) 920.8 km
c) 497.1 km/h

Q10 a) 8.13 m/s
b) 7.30 m/s

Q11 a) 220 km
b) 5 mins

Q12 180 m at 42 mph takes 4hrs 17 mins. 180 m at 64 mph takes 2 hrs 49 mins. So it stops for 1 hr 28 mins.

Q13 a) 4.9 m/s
b) 24.5 m/s
c) 14.7 m/s
d) 17.64 km/h, 88.2 km/h, 52.92 km/h.

Q14 122.5 s, 124.0 s, 127.5 s.

Q15 a) 0.75 g/cm³
b) 0.6 g/cm³
c) 0.8 g/cm³
d) 700 kg/m³ = 0.7 g/cm³

Q16 a) 62.4 g
b) 96 g
c) 3744 g (3.744 kg)
d) 75 g

Q17 a) 1176 cm³
b) 278 cm³ (to 3 s.f.)
c) 2500 cm³
d) 45 500 cm³ (to 3 s.f.)

Q18 34.71 g

Q19 20968 cm³

Q20 Vol. = 5000 cm³ = 5 litres

Q21 1.05 g/cm³

Q22 a) SR flour 1.16 g/cm³; granary flour 1.19 g/cm³
b) 378 ml

Q23 2.7 g/cm³

Q24 165.23 g

Q25 150 N/m²

Q26 0.8 m²

Q27 448 N

Q28 30.59 cm

Section Five — Geometry and Measures

Page 73 — Geometry

Q1 a) $x = 47$
b) $y = 154$
c) $z = 22$

d) $p = 35$, $q = 45$

Q2 a) $a = 146$
b) $m = 131$, $z = 48$
c) $x = 68$, $p = 112$
d) $s = 20$, $t = 90$

Q3 a) $x = 96$, $p = 38$
b) $a = 108$, $b = 23$, $c = 95$
c) $d = 120$, $e = 60$, $f = 60$, $g = 120$
d) $h = 155$, $i = 77.5$, $j = 102.5$, $k = 77.5$

Q4 a) $b = 70$ $c = 30$
  $d = 50$ $e = 60$
  $f = 150$
b) $g = 21$ $h = 71$
  $i = 80$ $j = 38$
  $k = 92$
c) $l = 35$ $m = 145$
  $n = 55$ $p = 125$

Q5 a) $x = 162$ $y = 18$
b) $x = 87$ $y = 93$
  $z = 93$
c) $a = 30$ $2a = 60$
  $5a = 150$ $4a = 120$

Page 74 — Parallel Lines

Q1 a) $a = 130°$
b) $b = 56°$
c) $c = 48°$

Q2 a) $d = 72°$, $e = 50°$
b) $f = 65°$, $g = 46°$
c) $h = 75°$, $i = 119°$, $j = 61°$

Q3 a) $a = 141°$, $b = 141°$, $c = 39°$, $d = 141°$, $e = 39°$
b) $a = 47°$, $b = 47°$, $c = 133°$, $d = 43°$, $e = 43°$
c) $m = 140°$, $n = 140°$, $p = 134°$, $q = 46°$, $r = 40°$

Q4 a) $x = 70°$
b) $x = 50°$
c) $x = 5°$

Page 75 — Polygons

Q1 Isosceles

Q2

order of rotational symmetry = 6

Q3 $540° - (100° + 104° + 120°)$
  $= 216°$ for two equal angles
  $\therefore 1$ angle = $108°$

Q4 a) $90° + 60° = 150°$

b)

$\angle PRW = 75°$

---

c) $180 - (360/n) = 150$
  $180n - 360 = 150n$
  $30n = 360 \Rightarrow n = 12$

Q5 a) Interior angle = $165°$
b) Exterior angle = $180° - 165° = 15°$
  Sum of exterior angles = $15° \times 24$
  $= 360°$

Q6 a)

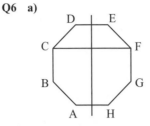

b) Angle CDE = angle DEF
  $= \dfrac{(8 - 2)180}{8} = 135°$
  So angle EFC (and angle DCF)
  $= \dfrac{360 - 2(135)}{2} = 45°$
  Or exterior angle = $45°$ = angle EFC, since EFC and an exterior angle are alternate angles.

Q7 $(n - 2) \times 180 = 2520$, $n = 16$

Q8 a) $(6 - 2) \times 180° = 720°$
b) $x + x + 2(x + 20°) + 2(x + 40°) = 720°$
  $6x + 120° = 720°$
  $6x = 600°$, $x = 100°$

Page 76 — Triangles and Quadrilaterals

Q1 a) Isosceles triangle
b) Kite
c) Right-angled triangle
d) Rhombus

Q2 $128°$, $52°$ and $128°$

Q3 a) Parallelogram, rhombus, (isosceles) trapezium
b) $32°$ and $116°$, or $74°$ and $74°$

Q4 $u = 120°$, $v = 150°$

Q5 a) $y = 20°$
b) $y = 36°$

Pages 77-78 — Circle Geometry

Q1 a) BAD = $80°$ (opposite angle C in cyclic quadrilateral)
b) EAB = $180 - 80 - 30 = 70°$

Q2 a) BD = 5 cm (as the tangents BD and CD are equal).
b) Angle COD = $70°$
  $(= 180° - (20° + 90°))$, since the tangent CD meets the radius OC at an angle of $90°$.
c) Angle COB = $140°$ (since angle BOD equals angle COD).
d) Angle CAB = $70°$ (since the angle at the centre (COB) is twice the angle at the circumference (CAB)).

Q3 a) BOE = $106°$ (angle at centre is twice the angle at the circumference)
b) ACE = $32°$ (alternate segment theorem)

Q4 a) ACD = $70°$ (alternate segment theorem)
b) BAD = $180 - (30 + 70) = 80°$

(opposite angles of a cyclic quadrilateral total $180°$)

Q5 a) Angles in the same segment.
b) $3x + 40 = 6x - 50$
  $90 = 3x$
  $30 = x$
  angle ABD = $3(30) + 40 = 130°$

Q6 a) By the alternate segment theorem, angle BCD = $29°$, so angle OCE = $90° - 29° = 61°$ (as a tangent meets a radius at $90°$). Then angle CEO = $61°$ as the triangle is isosceles (it's formed by 2 radii).
b) As OD goes through the centre of the circle, it must be the perpendicular bisector of CE, so angle EDO = $90°$.
c) Angle COD = $180° - 90° - 61° = 29°$

Q7 a) Angle ABD = $70°$ (angle at centre is twice the angle at the circumference)
b) Angle ABC = $90°$ (angle in semicircle)
c) Angle DBC = $20°$ (= $90° - 70°$)

Q8 a) $90°$ (angle in a semicircle)
b) The angle at A = $90°$ (tangent and radius are perpendicular). The third angle in the triangle is $180 - 90 - 23 = 67°$ and so $x = 90 - 67 = 23°$.
  Or, by alternate segment theorem: x = angle ABC = $23°$.

Q9 a) With AD as a chord, angle ABD = ACD = $30°$ (same segment); angle AXB = $85°$ (vertically opposite angles). The third angles must be the same in both triangles so the triangles must be similar.
b) Ratio of lengths = $\frac{4}{8} = \frac{1}{2}$
  so XB = 7.25 cm
c) Angle BDC = $180 - 85 - 30 = 65°$

Q10 Opposite angles in a cyclic quadrilateral add up to $180°$, so angle ABC = $180° - 92° = 88°$. The angle at the centre of a circle is twice the angle at the circumference, so if X is the centre, angle AXC should equal $88° \times 2 = 176°$. However, angle AXC = $178°$, so X cannot be the centre of the circle.

Page 79 — Congruent Shapes

Q1 ABC and DFE are congruent by SAS (two sides and the angle between them are the same).

Q2

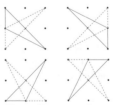

Hence 7 ways to draw another.

Q3 Sides AB and CD are the same, sides AM and CM are the same and sides BM and DM are the same (as M is the midpoint of the diagonals). So triangles ABM and CDM are congruent by SSS (all three sides are the same length).

Q4 Side OC is common to both triangles, sides OA and OB (the hypotenuses) are the same length as they are both radii and angle OCA = OCB = 90°. So triangles AOC and BOC are congruent by RHS (the right angle, hypotenuse and one other side match up).

Q5 Draw in the bisector of angle ABC and label point D where it meets AC.

This creates two triangles ABD and CBD. Side BD is common to both triangles. Angle ABC has been split in half, so angles ABD and DBC are equal. We know AB and BC are equal. Therefore triangles ABD and CBD are congruent by SAS, so angles CAB and BCA are equal.

Q6 Angles CDB and DBA are alternate angles and therefore equal. Angles DCA and CAB are alternate angles and are therefore equal. Side CE is the same length as side AE. So the triangles are congruent by AAS.

Page 80 — Similar Shapes

Q1 Angle BCD is common to both triangles. Angle EAC = angle DBC (corresponding angles). Angle AEC = angle BDC (corresponding angles). So the triangles are similar as all three angles are the same.

Q2 The triangles formed are similar, and $5 \div 1 = 5$, so the scale factor is 5. So the height of the statue is $30 \text{ cm} \times 5 = 150 \text{ cm}$ or 1.5 m.

Q3 **a)** Angle A shared. Parallel lines make corresponding angles equal so the triangles are similar as all three angles arc the same.

b) Ratio of lengths given by $\frac{AB}{AD} = \frac{12}{20} = \frac{3}{5}$

So $x = 25 \times \frac{3}{5} = 15$ cm

Also $\frac{y + 10}{y} = \frac{5}{3}$

$\Rightarrow 2y = 30$, $y = 15$ cm

Q4 **a)** Triangles APQ and STC (both isosceles and share angle A or C).

b) Ratio AC:AQ = 24:7.5 = 3.2:1 so $AP = 15 \times \frac{1}{3.2} = 4.6875$ cm $PT = 24 - 2 \ (4.6875) = 14.625$ cm

c) Using $\frac{1}{2} \times$ base $\times$ height $= \frac{1}{2}(24)(9) = 108$ cm²

d) Scale factor $= \frac{1}{3.2}$

Area scale factor $= \frac{1}{10.24}$

Area of triangle APQ $= 108 \times \frac{1}{10.24}$ $= 10.546... = 10.5$ cm² (to 3 s.f.)

e) $108 - 2 \ (10.546...) = 87$ cm² (to 2 s.f.)

Q5 **a)** All lengths must be enlarged in the same ratio for them to be similar.

b) 4 litres

Pages 81-82 — The Four Transformations

Q1 **a)** to **f)** — see diagram.

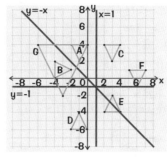

g) Rotation of 180°, centre (3, 0)

Q2 **a), b), d), e), f)** — see diagram

c) Rotation 180° about (0, 2).

g) 90° rotation anticlockwise about $\left(-\frac{1}{2}, -\frac{1}{2}\right)$, or 90° rotation clockwise about (-2, -6).

Q3 **a), b)** — see diagram.

c) Ratio of areas C:A = 1:4

Q4 **a), b), c)** — see diagram.

d) Rotation of 180° about (0, 0)

Q5 **a)**

b) $\overrightarrow{QO} = \begin{pmatrix} -3 \\ -4 \end{pmatrix}$

T $= \begin{pmatrix} 11 \\ 8 \end{pmatrix} + \begin{pmatrix} -3 \\ -4 \end{pmatrix} = \begin{pmatrix} 8 \\ 4 \end{pmatrix}$

see diagram

c) $\begin{pmatrix} -1 \\ 2 \end{pmatrix} + \begin{pmatrix} 8 \\ 4 \end{pmatrix} + \begin{pmatrix} -3 \\ -4 \end{pmatrix} + \begin{pmatrix} -4 \\ -2 \end{pmatrix} = \begin{pmatrix} 0 \\ 0 \end{pmatrix}$

Pages 83-84 — Perimeter and Area

Q1 **a)** l = 24, w = 12, area = 288 m²

b) 1 Carpet tile = 0.50 × 0.50 = 0.25 m² So 288 m² ÷ 0.25 = 1152 tiles are required.

c) £4.99 per m² => £4.99 for 4 tiles Total cost = (1152 ÷ 4) × 4.99 = £1437.12

Q2 Perimeter $= 4 \times \sqrt{9000}$ = 379.47 m (2 d.p.) Natasha ran: 11 × 379.47 = 4200 m (to nearest 100 m)

Q3 48 ÷ 5 = 9.6 m length. Area of 1 roll = 11 m × 0.5 m = 5.5 m². 48 m² ÷ 5.5 m² = $8\frac{8}{11}$ rolls of turf required. Of course 9 should be ordered.

Q4 Base length = 4773 ÷ 43 = 111 mm

Q5 Each square = 0.6 m × 0.6 m = 0.36 m². Total area of material = 6 × 0.36 = 2.16 m²

Q6 Area = ½ × 8.2 × 4.1 = 16.81 m² Perimeter = 10.8 + 4.474... + 8.2 = 23.5 m (to 3 s.f.)

Q7 Area of larger triangle = ½ × 14.4 × 10 = 72 cm² Area of inner triangle = ½ × 5.76 × 4 = 11.52 cm² Area of metal used for a bracket = 72 − 11.52 = 60.48 cm² so NO, bracket is too heavy for the fixing.

Q8

Area = 4 × Area of shaded triangle = 4 × (½ × 3.5 × 5.5) = 38.5 km²

Q9 T_1: ½ × 8 × 16 = 64 m² Tr_1: ½ × 8 × (8 + 16) = 96 m² Tr_2: ½ × 4 × (8 + 12) = 40 m² T_2: ½ × 8 × 12 = 48 m² Total area of glass sculpture = 248 m²

Q10 **a)** Area of each isosceles triangle = ½ × 2.3 × 3.2 = 3.68 m²

b) Area of each side = $(\sqrt{3.2^2 + 1.15^2}) \times 4 = 13.601...$ = 13.6 m² (to 3 s.f.) Groundsheet = 2.3 × 4 = 9.2 m²

c) Total material = 2 × 3.68 + 9.2 + 2 × 13.601... = 43.8 m² (to 3 s.f.)

Q11 **a)** Perimeter = $x + x + \frac{1}{2}x + x + x + \frac{1}{2}x$ = 5x cm

b) Area = $2x \times \frac{1}{2}x = x^2$ cm²

Q12 3x + 3 = 4x, so x = 3. Perimeter of trapezium = 39 cm.

Q13 Areas: $x^2 = y(3x + 1)$ Perimeters: 4x + 6 = 6x + 2 + 2y Solving these equations simultaneously gives x = -0.32, y = 2.32, or $x = 1.57$, $y = 0.43$ (correct to 2 d.p.). x and y must both be positive, so the solution is $x = 1.57$, $y = 0.43$.

Page 85 — Area — Circles

Q1 B = major sector
C = chord
D = tangent

Q2 a) 117.67 m² to 2 d.p.
b) 45.238... = 45 m to 2 s.f.
c) 46.5 m to 1 d.p.
d) 14.159... = 14.2 cm² to 3 s.f.

Q3 a) Area = area of a full circle radius 10 cm.
$A = \pi r^2 = \pi \times 10^2 = 314$ cm² to 3 s.f.
Circumference = $\pi \times D$
$= \pi \times 20 = 62.831...$ cm
So perimeter = 62.831... + 20
= 82.8 cm to 3 s.f.
b) Area = (area of a full circle radius 15 cm) + (area of a rectangle 15 × 30 cm) = $(\pi \times 15^2) + (15 \times 30)$
= 1156.9 cm² to 1 d.p.
Perimeter = (Circumference of a full circle radius 15 cm) + 15 + 15
= $(\pi \times 30) + 30 = 124.2$ cm to 1 d.p.
c) Area = Outer semi circle – Inner semi circle = 510.5 m² to 1 d.p.
Perimeter = ½ Circumference of outer + ½ Circumference of inner + 5 + 5
$= \frac{1}{2} \times \pi \times 70 + \frac{1}{2} \times \pi \times 60 + 10$
= 214.2 m to 1 d.p.

Q4 a) ABDC = $\frac{60}{360} \times \pi(30)^2 - \frac{60}{360} \times \pi(20)^2$
= 261.79... = 261.8 mm² (to 1 d.p.)
b) $2(\frac{1}{2}\pi 5^2) = 78.53...$ mm².
Hence 261.79... + 78.53...
= 340.3 mm² (to 1 d.p.)
c) Length of inner arc = $\frac{60}{360} \times \pi \times 20 \times 2$
= 20.943... mm
Length of outer arc = $\frac{60}{360} \times \pi \times 30 \times 2$
= 31.415... mm
Circumference of two semicircles
= $\pi \times 10 = 31.415...$ mm
Total perimeter = 20.943... + 31.415... + 31.415... = 83.8 mm (to 1 d.p.)

Q5 a) 80/360 × π × 5² = 17.453... cm²
= 17.45 cm² (to 2 d.p.)
b) Area of triangle AOB =
$\frac{1}{2} \times 5 \times 5 \times \sin 80° = 12.310...$
= 12.31 cm² (to 2 d.p.)
Shaded Area = 17.453... – 12.310...
= 5.14 cm² (to 2 d.p.)

Page 86 — 3D Shapes — Surface Area

Q1 No, Hannah would need more than 603 cm².

Q2 Surface area = $4 \times \pi \times 3^2$
= 113.10 cm² (to 2 d.p)

Q3 Surface area of cone = $\pi r l + \pi r^2$
= $(\pi \times 1.5 \times 8) + (\pi \times 1.5^2)$
= 44.77 cm² (to 2 d.p)
Height of triangular prism = $\sqrt{3^2 - 1.5^2}$
= $\sqrt{6.75}$ = 2.598... cm
Surface area of triangular prism =
$2(\frac{1}{2} \times 3 \times 2.598...) + 3(3 \times 8)$
= 79.79 cm² (to 2 d.p.)

Therefore the triangular prism has the greater surface area.

Q4 Surface area of hemisphere =
$\pi r^2 + \frac{1}{2}(4\pi r^2)$
$75\pi = 3\pi r^2$
$r^2 = 25$, radius = 5 cm

Q5 $AB^2 = 2^2 + 1.5^2$ AB = 2.5 m
1 panel on roof = $\frac{1}{2}AB \times \frac{5}{2}$
= 1.25 × 2.5 = 3.125 m²
Front of greenhouse = (2.5 × 4) + (½ × 4 × 1.5) = 13 m²
Total = 3.125 + 13 = 16.125 m²

Q6 a) Surface area = $4(½ \times 20 \times 31.6) + 20^2$
= 1664 m²
b) 1664 – 400 = 1264
1264 ÷ 15 = 84.266... so he will need 85 tins of paint

Pages 87-89 — 3D Shapes — Volume

Q1 a) $\frac{1}{2}\pi(0.35)^2 = 0.1924... = 0.192$ m²
b) 0.1924... × 3 = 0.577 m³

Q2 a) $\pi(2.5^2 - 2^2) = 7.07$ m²
£16 × 7.07 = £113.12 = £110 to nearest £10.
b) Volume = $\pi(2)^2 \times 0.50 = 6.28$ m³
6.28 × 15 = 94 ml to nearest ml

Q3 a) Volume Cube = Volume Cylinder
$10^3 = \pi r^2 \times 10$ so $r^2 = \frac{10^2}{\pi}$,
$r = 5.64$ cm
b) S.A. of cylinder = $2\pi r h + 2\pi r^2$ =
$2\pi \times 5.64... \times 10 + 2\pi \times (5.64...)^2$
= 554.49 cm²

Q4 a) $\pi(5)^2(16) = 1257$ cm³
b) $\pi(5)^2 h = 600$
$h = \frac{600}{25\pi} = 7.64$ cm

Q5 $(3)(3)(0.5) - \pi(0.7)^2(0.5) = 3.73$ cm³

Q6 Volume = $\frac{4}{3}\pi r^3 = \frac{4}{3} \times \pi \times 15^3$
= 14 137 cm³

Q7 Volume = $\frac{1}{3} \times (230 \times 230) \times 139$
= 2 451 033 m³

Q8 $(\pi \times (2)^2 \times 110) +$
$(½(14 + 20) \times 6 \times 20) = 3422.30$ cm³
2 × 3422.30 = 6844.60 cm³ = 6.84 l

Q9 a) (60)(30) + (30)(120) = 5400 cm²
b) 5400 × 100 = 540 000 cm³
= 0.54 m³

Q10 Volume of 1 bauble: $\frac{4}{3}\pi r^3 = \frac{4}{3} \times \pi \times 3^3$
= 113.097... cm³
5 ml per second = 5 cm³/s
Time taken to fill 1 bauble:
113.097... ÷ 5 = 22.619... seconds
Time taken to fill 10 baubles:
22.619... × 10 = 226.194... s
= 3 minutes and 46 seconds
(to the nearest second)

Q11 a) $\frac{1}{2}(\frac{4}{3}\pi(1.3)^3) + \pi(1.3)^2 \times 1.8$
$+ \frac{1}{3}\pi(1.3)^2 \times 1.2 = 16.28$ cm³
b) Volume of sand in hemisphere and cone parts remain the same so change is in cylindrical part.
Therefore $h + 0.3 = 1.8$,
$h = 1.5$ cm.

c) Volume of sand transferred =
$\frac{1}{2}(\frac{4}{3}\pi(1.3)^3) + \pi(1.3)^2 \times 1.5$
= 12.57 cm³
Time Taken = $\frac{12.57}{0.05} \approx 251$ secs.
= 4 minutes 11 secs

Q12 a) Volume of ice cream
$= \frac{1}{3}\pi(R^2H - r^2h) + \frac{1}{2}(\frac{4}{3}\pi R^3)$
$= \frac{1}{3}\pi(2.5^2 \times 10 - 1^2 \times 4)$
$+ \frac{1}{2}(\frac{4}{3}\pi \times 2.5^3)$
= 93.99 cm³ of ice cream.
b) Outer surface area of cone
$= \pi R l$
Using Pythagoras,
$l^2 = 10^2 + 2.5^2 = 106.25$,
$l = 10.3$ cm. So S.A. =
$\pi \times 2.5 \times 10.3 = 81.0$ cm²

Q13 Vol. increase is a cylinder of height 4.5 cm. So vol. increase =
$\pi(5)^2 \times 4.5 = 353.4$ cm³.
Volume of each marble = $\frac{353.4}{200}$
= 1.767 cm³
$\frac{4}{3}\pi r^3 = 1.767 => r = 0.75$ cm

Q14 a) $x(3 - x)(5 - x)$ m³
or $(x^3 - 8x^2 + 15x)$ m³
b)

X	0	1	2	3
V	0	8	6	0

c)

d) about 8.2 m³
e) ends   2(1.2)(1.8) =   4.32 +
side faces 2(1.2)(3.8) =   9.12 +
tops   2(3.8)(1.8) =   13.68
So surface area is about   27.12 m²
f) $x = 2$ or $x = 0.6$
If $x = 0.6$:
ends   2(0.6)(2.4) =   2.88 +
side faces 2(0.6)(4.4) =   5.28 +
tops   2(2.4)(4.4) = 21.12
29.28 m²
If $x = 2$:
ends   2(2)(1) =   4 +
side faces 2(2)(3) =   12 +
tops   2(1)(3) =   6
22 m²
Maximum Total S.A. ≈ 29.28 m²

Q15 a) The cross-section is a trapezium, so area = ½(5 + 11) × 4 = 32 cm²
b) 500 cm³ per minute = 8.333... cm³/s
Speed = 8.333... ÷ 32 = 0.260 cm/s
(3 s.f.)

Page 90 — More Enlargements

Q1 a) 2 end faces 2 × (2 × 3) = 12 cm²
2 side faces 2 × (5 × 3) = 30 cm²
Top & bottom 2 × (5 × 2) = 20 cm²
Total = 62 cm²
b) SF for length = 4
SF for area = 16
new area = 62 × 16 = 992 cm²

Q2 Widths in ratio 2:3, so
volumes in ratio 8:27.
Volume $= 30 \times \frac{27}{8} = 101$ litres

Q3 (scale factor)$^3 = 1200 \div 150 = 8$,
which means scale factor = 2
Surface area of small tin $= 600 \div 2^2$
$= 150$ cm^2

Q4 **a)** (scale factor)$^2 = 237.5 \div 38 = 6.25$,
which means scale factor = 2.5
Height of cuboid B $= 4 \times 2.5 = 10$ cm

b) Volume of cuboid B is $2.5^3 = 15.625$
times the volume of cuboid A (V_A).
$(V_A \div 15.625\,V_A) \times 100 = 6.4\%$

Q5 **a)** In m^3, the volume $= \frac{1}{3}\pi(1^2)(1)$

$= 1.0471...$ m^3
$= 1.05$ m^3 (to 3 s.f.)

b) 50 cm

c) ratio $= 1:2^3 = 1:8$

d) Volume of small cone =

$1.0471... \times \frac{1}{8} = 0.131$ m^3 (to 3 s.f.)

e) $\frac{1}{8}$ of original volume has been

removed, leaving $\frac{7}{8}$. So ratio is 7:1.

Page 91 — Projections

Q1 **a)** Front elevation:

b) Side elevation:

c) Plan:

Q2

Q3 Using a scale of 1 cm = 1 m, your
drawing should be as below:

Q4

Plan view

Front elevation   Side elevation

Pages 92-93 — Loci and Construction

Q1

Not to scale

Q2 **a)** and **b)**

Not to scale

Q3 **a)** and **b)**

Not to scale

Length BA = 0.9 cm (accept 0.8 cm)

Q4

Not to scale

Q5 **a)** and **b)**

Not to scale
Radius of the circle = 2.7 cm

Q6 **a)** A circle with diameter AB.
b) and **c)**

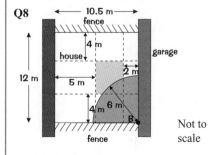

Not to scale

d) The ship comes 1.7 cm = 0.85 km
from the rock.

Q7 **a)**

32.5 m 32.5 m 32.5 m
A ——— 100 m ——— B
32.5 m

b) Distance around dashed path =
$(2 \times 100) + (\pi \times 65) = 404.2$ m

Q8

fence 10.5 m
4 m
house   garage
12 m
5 m   2 m
4 m 6 m
B
4 m
fence   Not to scale

Q9 **a)**

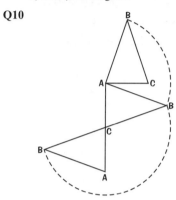

b) Length = 8.6 cm equivalent to 43 km
(accept 44 km).

c) 35 km in 2.5 hrs, so speed
$= \frac{35}{2.5} = 14$ km/h

d) and **e)** see diagram

Q10

Page 94 — Bearings

Q1 **a)** 245°   **b)** 310°
c) 035°   **d)** 131°
e) 297°, 028°, 208°

Q2 **a)**

boat
040°   350 m
coast-
guard   50°
tree

i) 268 m (accept 265-271)
ii) 225 m (accept 222-228)

b) $350^2 = 122\,500$
$225^2 + 268^2 = 122\,449$

Q3

a) 96 km (accept 94-98)
b) 255 km (accept 253-257)
c) 266 km (accept 264-268)
d) 156° (accept 154-158)
e) 082° (accept 080-084)
f) 177° (accept 175-179)

150

Q4 start 165°
    1200 m
    210°
    1500 m
    finish
    2500 m (accept 2450-2550),
    010° (accept 008-012)

Section Six — Pythagoras and Trigonometry

Pages 95-97 — Pythagoras' Theorem

Q1 a) 10.8 cm   f) 7.89 m
    b) 6.10 m   g) 9.60 cm
    c) 5 cm   h) 4.97 cm
    d) 27.0 mm   i) 6.80 cm
    e) 8.49 m   j) 8.5 cm

Q2 a = 3.32 cm   f = 8.62 m
    b = 6 cm   g = 6.42 m
    c = 6.26 m   h = 19.2 mm
    d = 5.6 mm   i = 9.65 m
    e = 7.08 mm   j = 48.7 mm

Q3 k = 6.55 cm   q = 7.07 cm
    l = 4.87 m   r = 7.50 m
    m = 6.01 m   s = 9.45 mm
    n = 12.4 cm   t = 4.33 cm
    p = 5.22 cm   u = 7.14 m

Q4 9.7 m

Q5 a) 12 cm, 7.94 cm
    b) 40.9 cm
    c) 89.7 cm^2

Q6 314 m

Q7 91.9 cm

Q8 5.0 m

Q9 4.58 m

Q10 AB: 5 (don't need Pythagoras)
    CD: $\sqrt{10} = 3.16$
    EF: $\sqrt{13} = 3.61$
    GH: $\sqrt{8} = 2.83$
    JK: $\sqrt{5} = 2.24$
    LM: $\sqrt{26} = 5.10$
    PQ: $\sqrt{20} = 4.47$
    RS: $\sqrt{45} = 6.71$
    TU: $\sqrt{13} = 3.61$

Q11 a) i) 5
       ii) $\sqrt{17} = 4.12$
       iii) 5
       iv) $\sqrt{58} = 7.62$
       v) $\sqrt{26} = 5.10$
    b) parallelogram

Q12 a) $\sqrt{41} = 6.40$
    b) $\sqrt{98} = 9.90$
    c) $\sqrt{53} = 7.28$
    d) $\sqrt{34} = 5.83$
    e) 4 (don't need Pythagoras here)
    f) $\sqrt{37} = 6.08$

Q13 a) $\sqrt{10} = 3.16$
    b) $\sqrt{130} = 11.40$
    c) $\sqrt{8} = 2.83$
    d) $\sqrt{233} = 15.26$
    e) $\sqrt{353} = 18.79$
    f) 10

Q14 192 km

Q15
    7 km
    finish
    12 km
    start
    13.9 km from the starting point.

Q16 Right-angled triangle with shorter sides of length 2 and 3 units. E.g.

Pages 98-100 — Trigonometry — Sin, Cos, Tan

	(tan)	(sin)	(cos)
Q1 a)	0.306	0.292	0.956
b)	8.14	0.993	0.122
c)	0.0875	0.0872	0.996
d)	0.532	0.469	0.883
e)	1	0.707	0.707

Q2 a = 1.40 cm   c = 5.31 cm
    b = 6 cm   d = 10.8 cm
    θ = 28.1°

Q3 e = 12.6 cm   g = 6.71 m
    f = 11.3 cm   h = 30.1 cm
    θ = 49.5°

Q4 i = 4.89 cm   k = 5.32 cm
    j = 3.79 cm   l = 41.6 cm
    θ = 52.4°

Q5 m = $5\sqrt{3}$ cm   s = 9.5 cm
    n = $10\sqrt{3}$ cm   t = $\frac{116\sqrt{3}}{3}$ cm
    p = 11.5 cm   u = $\frac{58\sqrt{3}}{3}$ cm
    q = $\frac{23\sqrt{3}}{2}$ cm   v = $\frac{33\sqrt{2}}{4}$ cm
    r = $\frac{19\sqrt{2}}{2}$ cm   w = $\frac{33\sqrt{2}}{4}$ cm

Q6 a) 30
        hypotenuse   40
        50
    b) 36.9°

Q7 a) P 3 Q
       (1,2)   (4,2)
       5.83   5
       R
       (4,-3)

b) 59.0°
c) 31.0°

Q8 a)

    b) 71.6°
    c) 36.9°
    d) 71.6°

Q9 2.1 m

Q10 62°

Q11 20.5°

Q12

    base
    9 km
    θ
    7 km boat
    θ = 52.1°, bearing = 322°

Q13 a) both 30.8 cm
    b) 27.5 cm   c) 385 cm^2

Q14

    65°
    7 cm   7 cm
    h
    base
    height = 5.90, base = 7.52,
    so area = 22.2 cm^2.

Q15 a) $5\sqrt{3}$ cm
    b) 5 cm
    c) $25\sqrt{3}$ cm^2

Q16 a) 10.8 cm
    b) 150.8 cm^2 c) 21.0°

Q17
    16°
    ?
    1020 m   1235 m
    750 m

Q18 b = 14.4 m

Q19 $\sin 60° + \cos 45° = \frac{\sqrt{3}}{2} + \frac{1}{\sqrt{2}}$
    $= \frac{\sqrt{3}}{2} + \frac{1 \times \sqrt{2}}{\sqrt{2} \times \sqrt{2}} = \frac{\sqrt{3}}{2} + \frac{\sqrt{2}}{2}$
    $= \frac{\sqrt{3} + \sqrt{2}}{2}$

Q20

    ship
    100 km
    light-house
    ?   300° start
    86.6 km

Answers

Pages 101-103 — The Sine and Cosine Rules

Q1
$a = 4.80$ cm	$f = 5.26$ cm
$b = 25.8$ mm	$g = 9.96$ cm
$c = 13.0$ cm	$h = 20.2$ mm
$d = 8.89$ m	$i = 3.72$ m
$e = 18.4$ cm	$j = 8.29$ cm

Q2
$k = 51°$	$r = 64°$
$l = 46°$	$s = 18°$
$m = 43°$	$t = 49°$
$p = 45°$	$u = 88°$
$q = 36°$	

Q3
$a = 135°$	$c = 98°$
$b = 132°$	

Q4
$a = 63°$	$f = 5.6$ cm
$b = 45°$	$g = 49°$
$c = 8.9$ cm	$h = 78°$
$d = 27°$	$i = 5.0$ mm
$e = 10.5$ cm	

Q5 a) 46°   b) 52°   c) 82°

Q6 12.0 m

Q7 a) 28.8 km   b) 295.5°

Q8

Diagonals 11.2 cm and 6.6 cm.

Q9

Distance = 1.2 miles.
The alarm should be ringing because the planes are less than 3 miles apart, so the software seems reliable.

Q10 a) 16.9 m
b) 12.4 m
c) 25.8 m
d) 19.5 m

Q11

a) 86°
b) 323 km
c) 215°

Q12 a)

7.1 cm

b)

14.5 cm
(118.5° comes from the fact that the minute hand is at 19.75 mins.
$19.75 \div 60 \times 360 = 118.5$)

c)

13.5 cm

Q13 35 mm

Q14

Mary's string = 5.85 m
Jane's string = 7.13 m

Q15 a) 18.1 cm²   d) 29.5 m²
b) 8.5 m²   e) 25.5 cm²
c) 198.6 cm²   f) 13.4 mm²

Q16 a) 963.9 m²   d) 52.6 m²
b) 17.4 m²   e) 9.2 mm²
c) 7.9 cm²   f) 15.1 cm²

Q17 a) Area of patio = 115.1 m², so area of grass = 164.9 m²
b) Length AC = 24.5 m, so length CD = 14.3 m

Q18 a) 0.65 m²
b) $x = 1.4$

Page 104 — 3D Pythagoras and Trigonometry

Q1 a) 59.0°   c) 25 cm
b) 23.3 cm   d) 21.1°

Q2 a) 42.5 cm   b) 50.9 cm

Q3 a) 36.1 cm, 21.5 cm, 31.0 cm
b) 36.9 cm

Q4 The 85p box

Q5 a) 3.82 cm
b) 45.8 cm²
c) 137.5 cm³

Q6 a) $\sqrt{208} + \sqrt{89} + \sqrt{169} = 36.9$ cm
b) 39.8°
c) 60.0 cm²

Pages 105-106 — Vectors

Q1 a)

b) i) $\begin{pmatrix} -1 \\ -4 \end{pmatrix}$ ii) $\begin{pmatrix} 4 \\ 0 \end{pmatrix}$ iii) $\begin{pmatrix} 5 \\ 4 \end{pmatrix}$
c) Isosceles

Q2 a) $\begin{pmatrix} 2 \\ 1 \end{pmatrix}$ $\underset{\sim}{p} + \underset{\sim}{q}$

b) $\begin{pmatrix} 2 \\ 5 \end{pmatrix}$ $\underset{\sim}{p} - \underset{\sim}{q}$

c) $\begin{pmatrix} 6 \\ -2 \end{pmatrix}$ $2\underset{\sim}{r}$

d) $\begin{pmatrix} 1 \\ 1 \end{pmatrix}$ $\underset{\sim}{s} + \underset{\sim}{p}$

e) $\begin{pmatrix} 6 \\ 10 \end{pmatrix}$ $2\underset{\sim}{p} - 2\underset{\sim}{s}$

f) $\begin{pmatrix} -1 \\ -8 \end{pmatrix}$ $3\underset{\sim}{q} + \underset{\sim}{s}$

g) $\begin{pmatrix} 6 \\ 0 \end{pmatrix}$ $2\underset{\sim}{r} - \underset{\sim}{q}$

h) $\begin{pmatrix} 6 \\ -3 \end{pmatrix}$ $\frac{1}{2}\underset{\sim}{q} + 2\underset{\sim}{r}$

i) $\begin{pmatrix} 0 \\ -1 \end{pmatrix}$ $\underset{\sim}{p} + 2\underset{\sim}{s}$

j) $\begin{pmatrix} -6 \\ 0 \end{pmatrix}$ $\underset{\sim}{q} - 2\underset{\sim}{r}$

Q3 a) $2\underset{\sim}{y}$ d) $2\underset{\sim}{y} + 2\underset{\sim}{x}$
b) $\underset{\sim}{y} + \underset{\sim}{x}$ e) $4\underset{\sim}{y} + 2\underset{\sim}{x}$
c) $-\underset{\sim}{y} - \underset{\sim}{x}$ f) $2\underset{\sim}{x}$

Q4 $\underset{\sim}{l} = \underset{\sim}{j} + 2\underset{\sim}{k}$
$\underset{\sim}{m} = -\underset{\sim}{j} + \underset{\sim}{k}$
$\underset{\sim}{n} = -2\underset{\sim}{j}$

Q5 a) $\overrightarrow{XY} = -\frac{3}{2}\underset{\sim}{a} + 2\underset{\sim}{b}$
b) $\overrightarrow{XZ} = \frac{5}{2}\underset{\sim}{a} - \underset{\sim}{b}$

Q6 a) i) $\overrightarrow{ED}$ or $\overrightarrow{AF}$ v) $\overrightarrow{BE}$
ii) $\overrightarrow{EF}$ or $\overrightarrow{DC}$ vi) $\overrightarrow{AC}$
iii) $\overrightarrow{AE}$ or $\overrightarrow{FD}$ vii) $\overrightarrow{EC}$ or $\overrightarrow{AB}$
iv) $\overrightarrow{BA}$ viii) $\overrightarrow{EB}$
b) i) 48 cm²   ii) 60 cm²

Answers

Q7 $\overrightarrow{AB} = -2\underset{\sim}{a} - 4\underset{\sim}{b}$

$\overrightarrow{DC} = -\underset{\sim}{a} - 2\underset{\sim}{b}$

$\overrightarrow{AB} = 2\overrightarrow{DC}$

$\overrightarrow{AB}$ is a scalar multiple of $\overrightarrow{DC}$, so the vectors must be parallel.

Q8 $\overrightarrow{FG} = 2\underset{\sim}{x} + 4\underset{\sim}{y}$

Q9 $\overrightarrow{NR} = \frac{27}{4}\underset{\sim}{a} + 9\underset{\sim}{b}$

Q10 $\overrightarrow{EG} = -\frac{3}{5}\underset{\sim}{a} + \frac{6}{5}\underset{\sim}{b}$

Q11 a) i) $2\underset{\sim}{a}$ **ii)** $\underset{\sim}{b} - 2\underset{\sim}{a}$ **iii)** $\underset{\sim}{a} - \underset{\sim}{b}$

b) $\overrightarrow{AC} = -2\underset{\sim}{b} + 2\underset{\sim}{a} = 2(\underset{\sim}{a} - \underset{\sim}{b}) = 2\overrightarrow{PQ}$

Since $\overrightarrow{AC}$ is a multiple of $\overrightarrow{PQ}$ they must both be in the same direction and therefore parallel.

Section Seven — Probability and Statistics

Page 107 — Probability Basics

Q1 a) $\frac{1}{2}$ **c)** $\frac{1}{6}$

b) $\frac{2}{3}$ **d)** 0

And so the letters should be arranged <u>approximately</u> like this on the number line.

Q2 The probability of a head is still $\frac{1}{2}$.

Q3 a) $\frac{5}{12}$ **c)** $\frac{3}{12} = \frac{1}{4}$

b) $\frac{4}{12} = \frac{1}{3}$ **d)** $\frac{9}{12} = \frac{3}{4}$

Q4 $1 - 0.27 = 0.73$ or $\frac{73}{100}$

Q5 a) $\frac{40}{132} = \frac{10}{33}$

b) P(car being blue or green) $= \frac{45}{132}$

P(not blue or green) $= \frac{87}{132} = \frac{29}{44}$

Q6 Debbie's chance of winning would be $\frac{1}{9}$. This is greater than 0.1, so she would choose to play.

Q7 $1 - (5 - 4y) = 4y - 4$

Q8 a) $x = 0.02$ **b)** 0.48

Page 108 — Counting Outcomes

Q1 a) (1,1), (1,2), (1,3), (1,4), (1,5), (1,6), (1,7), (2,1), (2,2), (2,3), (2,4), (2,5), (2,6), (2,7), (3,1), (3,2), (3,3), (3,4), (3,5), (3,6), (3,7)

b)

	1	2	3	4	5	6	7
1	2	3	4	5	6	7	8
2	3	4	5	6	7	8	9
3	4	5	6	7	8	9	10

c) $\frac{1}{7}$ **e)** $\frac{2}{7}$

d) $\frac{11}{21}$ **f)** $\frac{5}{7}$

Q2

	1	2	3	4	5
1	1,1	1,2	1,3	1,4	1,5
2	2,1	2,2	2,3	2,4	2,5
3	3,1	3,2	3,3	3,4	3,5
4	4,1	4,2	4,3	4,4	4,5
5	5,1	5,2	5,3	5,4	5,5
6	6,1	6,2	6,3	6,4	6,5

a) $\frac{1}{30}$

b) $\frac{2}{30} = \frac{1}{15}$

c) $\frac{6}{30} = \frac{1}{5}$

Q3 a) 3

b) $3 \times 3 \times 3 \times 3 \times 3 = 243$

c) $\frac{243}{100\,000} = 0.00243$

Q4 a) $3 \times 5 \times 2 = 30$

b) $(3 \times 5) + (3 \times 2) + (5 \times 2)$
$= 15 + 6 + 10 = 31$

Pages 109-110 — Probability Experiments

Q1 a)

Outcome	Frequency
W	8
D	5
L	7

b) The 3 outcomes are not equally likely.

c) $\frac{5}{20} = \frac{1}{4}$

d) They are most likely to win.

e) 14

Q2 a) $\frac{2}{5}$ **c)** $\frac{2}{3}$

b) $\frac{4}{15}$ **d)** 12

Q3 a) $\frac{14}{40} = \frac{7}{20} = 0.35$

b) $\frac{24}{60} = \frac{2}{5} = 0.4$

c) $\frac{38}{100} = \frac{19}{50} = 0.38$

Q4 a) $\frac{13}{150}$ **b)** $\frac{4}{80} = \frac{1}{20} = 0.05$

c) i) The red dice looks more likely to be biased. If you rolled an unbiased dice 250 times you would expect each of the 10 numbers to come up 25 times, but on the red dice, 10 came up 38 times, which is 13 more than you'd expect.

ii) You could gather more data by carrying out more rolls of the dice and seeing if the red dice continued to land on 10 more frequently than expected.

Q5 a) 8 **b)** 40 **c)** $\frac{43}{80}$

d) They'd each get closer to $\frac{1}{10}$.

Q6 a)

b) $\frac{9}{50}$

c) 11 (to the nearest whole number)

Q7 a) Ed's, because he has carried out the experiment more times.

b) Using Ed's results, the probability the toast landed buttered side down is $\frac{28}{62} = \frac{14}{31}$. So the probability of both landing buttered side down is $\frac{14}{31} \times \frac{14}{31} = \frac{196}{961} = 0.204$ (to 3 d.p.).

(Or you could estimate the probability by combining Kristina and Ed's results — this gives a probability of $\left(\frac{34}{70}\right)^2 = 0.236$ (to 3 d.p.).)

Page 111 — The AND / OR Rules

Q1 a) 0.0625

b) 0.1875

Q2 a) $\frac{10}{20} = \frac{1}{2}$

b) $\frac{4}{20} = \frac{1}{5}$

c) i) The events are not mutually exclusive (i.e. they can both happen together, since 5 and 15 are odd numbers and multiples of 5) — so P(A and B) does not equal zero.

ii) $\frac{12}{20} = \frac{3}{5}$

d) P(multiple of 3) $= \frac{6}{20}$

P(even number) $= \frac{10}{20}$

P(multiple of 3 and even) $= \frac{3}{20}$

So P(multiple of 3 or even number)

$= \frac{6}{20} + \frac{10}{20} - \frac{3}{20} = \frac{13}{20}$

Q3 P(no six in 1 roll) $= \frac{5}{6} = 0.83...$

P(no sixes in 2 rolls)
$= \left(\frac{5}{6}\right)^2 = \frac{25}{36} = 0.69...$

P(no sixes in 3 rolls)
$= \left(\frac{5}{6}\right)^3 = \frac{125}{216} = 0.57...$

P(no sixes in 4 rolls)
$= \left(\frac{5}{6}\right)^4 = \frac{625}{1296} = 0.48...$

So 4 times.

Q4 a) $\frac{7}{12}$ **b)** $\frac{5}{12}$

c) The two events are not mutually exclusive — they can both happen at the same time, since 3 is a white.

Q5 a) $\frac{2}{52} + \frac{2}{52} = \frac{1}{13}$

b) i) $\frac{1}{2} \times \frac{1}{52} = \frac{1}{104}$

ii) $\frac{1}{52} \times \frac{1}{2} = \frac{1}{104}$

iii) $\frac{1}{104} + \frac{1}{104} = \frac{2}{104} = \frac{1}{52}$

Q6 a) P(green then blue)
$= \frac{n}{16} \times \frac{16-n}{15} = \frac{16n-n^2}{240}$

b) Because the probability of getting a blue card with the second pick depends on whether or not a green card was selected with the first pick.

c) P(blue then green)
$= \frac{16-n}{16} \times \frac{n}{15} = \frac{16n-n^2}{240}$

So P(one card of each colour)

$= 2 \times \dfrac{16n - n^2}{240} = 0.4$

i.e. $n^2 - 16n + 48 = 0$

i.e. $(n - 12)(n - 4) = 0$

i.e. $n = 12$ or $n = 4$.

But since more than half the cards are green, $n = 12$.

Page 112 — Tree Diagrams

Q1

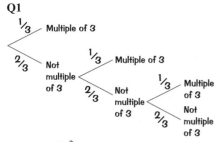

$1 - \left(\dfrac{2}{3}\right)^2 = 0.555...,$

but $1 - \left(\dfrac{2}{3}\right)^3 = 0.703...,$ so 3 times.

Q2

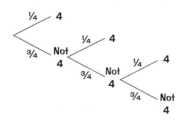

a) $\dfrac{3}{16}$

b) $\dfrac{37}{64}$

Q3 a) $\dfrac{1}{4}$ b) $\dfrac{1}{2}$ c) $\dfrac{1}{2}$

Q4 a)

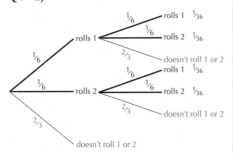

So P(total = 2 after 2 rolls)

$= \dfrac{4}{36} = \dfrac{1}{9}$

b)

So P(total = 3 after 1 or 2 rolls)

$= \left(4 \times \dfrac{1}{36}\right) + \left(2 \times \dfrac{1}{6}\right) = \dfrac{4}{9}$

Page 113 — Conditional Probability

Q1 a)

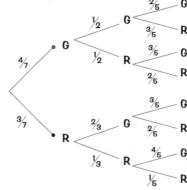

b) $\dfrac{18}{35}$

c) $\dfrac{3}{7}$

Q2 P(Jo sleeps well and runs well)

$= \dfrac{2}{3} \times 0.8 = \dfrac{2}{3} \times \dfrac{4}{5} = \dfrac{8}{15}$

Q3 a)

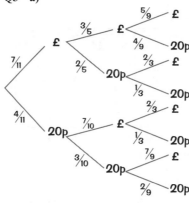

b) $\dfrac{28}{55}$ c) $\dfrac{46}{165}$

Q4 a) $\dfrac{1}{13}$ c) $\dfrac{36}{143}$

b) $\dfrac{83}{143}$ d) $\dfrac{6}{143}$

Pages 114-115 — Sets and Venn Diagrams

Q1 a) 5   c) 8

b) 2, 4, 7, 8   d) 3, 5, 9

Q2

Q3 a)

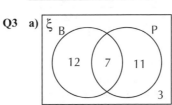

b) i) $\dfrac{19}{33}$

ii) $\dfrac{15}{33} = \dfrac{5}{11}$

Q4 a) 3, 9, 15

b)

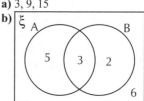

c) i) $\dfrac{8}{16} = \dfrac{1}{2}$ ii) $\dfrac{3}{16}$

iii) $\dfrac{11}{16}$

Q5 a)

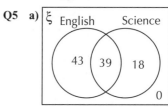

b) $\dfrac{39}{57} = \dfrac{13}{19}$

Q6 a) $x^2 + 2x + 22 = 121$

So $x^2 + 2x - 99 = 0$

i.e. $(x + 11)(x - 9) = 0$

This means $x = 9$.

b) $\dfrac{22}{121} = \dfrac{2}{11}$

c) $\dfrac{2}{7}$

Q7 a) $c = 6.24$

b) $c = 1.30$ (to 2 d.p.)

Page 116 — Sampling and Bias

Q1 a) All 20- to 30-year-old women

b) All the public parks in London

c) All the squirrels in Britain

d) All football players in the Premier League

Q2 a) All the moorland dung beetles in the UK

b) Because it would be extremely difficult and impractical for him to be sure that he had surveyed every single moorland dung beetle in the UK.

Q3 E.g. Reason 1 — the average wage of three people who are the same age might not be representative of the whole population (e.g. a 16-year-old may earn less than a 19-year-old).

Reason 2 — the sample is too small, so it won't be representative of the whole population.

Q4 a) People in a newsagent's are likely to be there to buy a newspaper.

b) At that time on a Sunday, people who go to church are likely to be at church.

Q5 a) The sample is not random and so might not be representative of all the cakes.

b) Number all the cakes from 1 to 50, reading across each row. Generate 5 random numbers (e.g. using a calculator, computer program or by picking numbers out of a bag) between 1 and 50. Select the 5 cake weights that correspond to the 5 numbers you have generated.

Q6 **a)** 315
b) The people in the two schools might be very different and have very different television viewing habits. This would mean his combined sample may not represent either school fairly.

Page 117 — Collecting Data

Q1 **a)** Qualitative **c)** Quantitative
b) Quantitative **d)** Qualitative

Q2 **a)** Discrete **c)** Discrete
b) Continuous **d)** Continuous

Q3 E.g.

Length of time (mins)	1-10	11-20	21-30	31-40	41-50
Number of people	5	10	5	5	5

Q4 **a)** There is no time period specified / the question is subjective – "very often" can mean different things to different people.
b) Any sensible answer with tick boxes, e.g. "How many times a week do you visit the school canteen? None, 1-2 times, 3-4 times or more than 4 times."

Q5 **a)** The question is ambiguous because the age classes overlap, e.g. someone who's 30 could go in either the 18-30 or 30-40 group.
b) Change the answers to:
Under 18, 18 to 30, 31 to 40, 41 to 60, over 60

Pages 118-119 — Mean, Median, Mode and Range

Q1 3 tries
Q2 mean = 1.333 (to 3 d.p.)
median = 1.5
mode = 2
range = 11
Q3 **a)** 3.5 **b)** 3.5 **c)** 5
Q4 **a)** 0 minutes
b) 0 minutes
c) 0 minutes
d) No, according to the raw data.
Q5 **a)** 22 **b)** 74
Q6 73.5 kg
Q7 20 kg
Q8 97%
Q9 **a)** Both spend a mean of 2 hours.
b) The range for Jim is 3 hours and for Bob is 2 hours.
c) The amount of TV that Jim watches each night is more variable than the amount that Bob watches.
Q10 **a)** 1 day **b)** 2 days
c) The statement is true according to the data, since 68 out of 88 (= 77%) of the cards arrive within 2 days.
Q11 2 (for 8, 8, 8, 9, 9, 10, 10)
Q12 6 (for 2, 2, 6, 7, 8)

Pages 120-121 — Frequency Tables — Finding Averages

Q1 **a)**

Subject	Frequency
Maths	5
English	7
French	3
Art	4
Science	6

b) 36 French lessons
c) English

Q2 **a)** 12 **b)** 12

Q3

Length (m)	Frequency
4 and under	3
6	5
8	6
10	4
12	1
14 and over	1

a) 8 m **b)** 8 m **c)** 14 m

Q4 **a)** 52 kg
b) 53 kg
c) 4 kg
d)

Weight (kg)	Frequency	Weight × Frequency
51	40	2040
52	30	1560
53	45	2385
54	10	540
55	5	275

So mean = 52.3 kg (to nearest 0.1 kg)

Q5 mean = 3.75
mode = 3
median = 4

Q6 **a)** 4 **b)** 3 **c)** 3.2 (to 1 d.p.)

Q7 **a)** False, mode is 8.
b) False, they are equal.
c) True

Page 122 — Grouped Frequency Tables

Q1 **a)**

Weight (w, in kg)	Tally	Frequency (f)
200≤w<250	IIII	4
250≤w<300	₩	5
300≤w<350	₩ IIII	9
350≤w<400	II	2

b) $300 \le w < 350$ kg
c) $300 \le w < 350$ kg

Q2 **a)**

Speed (s, in km/h)	40≤s<45	45≤s<50	50≤s<55	55≤s<60	60≤s<65
Frequency	4	8	10	7	3
Mid-Interval	42.5	47.5	52.5	57.5	62.5
Frequency × Mid-Interval	170	380	525	402.5	187.5

Estimated mean = 52.0 km/h
b) 22 skiers **c)** 62.5%

Q3 **a)** $0 \le n < 0.2$ and $0.4 \le n < 0.6$
b) $0.4 \le n < 0.6$
c) 0.483 s (to 3 d.p.)
d) 18 out of 48 = 37.5% of the times are less than 0.4 s.
[Either] Less than 40% of the times are below 0.4 s, so the claim is incorrect. [Or] Rounding the percentage to one significant figure,

40% of the times are less than 0.4 s, so the claim is correct.

Pages 123-124 — Box Plots

Q1 **a)** 75% **b)** 50
c) The interquartile range. This can be a more reliable measure of how spread out the data is because it's not affected by outliers.

Q2 **a)** 1020 – 80 = 940
b) 510
c) 700
d) 840
e)

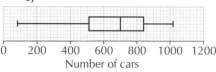

Q3 **a)** 65 g
b) $Q_1 = 60$ g and $Q_3 = 68$ g
c)

Q4 **a)**

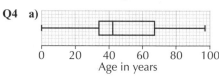

b) No, since none of the facts contain any information about the number of people in Polygonia.

Q5 **a)** *Run For Your Life* and *Fear Like You've Never Known Before*
b) E.g. The interquartile range for *Scream For All You're Worth* is lower than that for *Fear Like You've Never Known Before*, showing the number of visitors was more consistent from day to day.
The maximum and minimum values for *Fear Like You've Never Known Before* and *Scream For All You're Worth* are very similar, showing that the quietest and the busiest days on each ride involved similar numbers of people.
c) *Ride of Ghastly Terrors* — its median number of visitors is the smallest.
d) *Scream For All You're Worth* — its median number of visitors is the largest.

Q6 **a)** Minimum mark = 1.2
Maximum mark = 2.7
Median mark = 2.2
Lower quartile mark = 1.6
Upper quartile mark = 2.4
b)

c) The marks for the impressionist seem to be generally higher than those for the singer — the median, maximum, minimum and quartiles are all higher for the impressionist.

The spread of the data is also greater for the impressionist, showing that these marks varied much more than the marks for the singer did.

Pages 125-126 — Cumulative Frequency

Q1 Accept:
a) 133-134   **c)** 136-137
b) 127-128   **d)** 8-10

Q2 a)

Number of passengers, n	$0 \leq n < 50$	$50 \leq n < 100$	$100 \leq n < 150$	$150 \leq n < 200$	$200 \leq n < 250$	$250 \leq n < 300$
Frequency	2	7	10	5	3	1
Cumulative Frequency	2	9	19	24	27	28
Mid-Interval	25	75	125	175	225	275
Frequency × Mid-Interval	50	525	1250	875	675	275

Estimated mean = 130.4 passengers

b)

accept median of 118-128 passengers
c) $100 \leq n < 150$

Q3 a)

Mark (m%)	$0 \leq m < 20$	$20 \leq m < 40$	$40 \leq m < 60$	$60 \leq m < 80$	$80 \leq m < 100$
Frequency	2	12	18	5	3
Cumulative Frequency	2	14	32	37	40

b) 33%-38%
c) 19%-26%
d) 44%-47.5%
e) 52%-56%

Q4 a) $61 \leq t < 71$
b) $61 \leq t < 71$

c)

Time (t, mins)	Frequency	Cumulative frequency
$31 \leq t < 41$	4	4
$41 \leq t < 51$	12	16
$51 \leq t < 61$	21	37
$61 \leq t < 71$	32	69
$71 \leq t < 81$	19	88
$81 \leq t < 91$	8	96
$91 \leq t < 101$	4	100

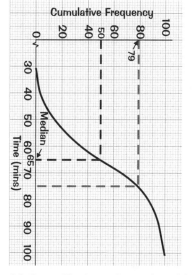

Median = 65 minutes (approximately)
d) Approximately 21
e) It assumes that the times in the $71 \leq t < 81$ class are distributed in such a way that the number of times less than 75 minutes can be read directly from the graph.

Q5 a) Approximately 31 (=120 – 89)
b) Approximately 7%
c) Approximately 76 bulbs had a lifetime of more than 1100 hours. So approximately 63% of the bulbs had a lifetime of more than 1100 hours — this means the data does not back up the managing director's claim.

Pages 127-129 — Histograms and Frequency Density

Q1 4 × 10 = 40 people

Q2

Q3 a) See graph.
b) Frequency for $150 < x \leq 200 = 275$

c)

Q4 a)

Weight (kg)	$0 \leq w < 2$	$2 \leq w < 4$	$4 \leq w < 7$	$7 \leq w < 9$	$9 \leq w < 15$
Frequency	3	2	6	9	12
Frequency density	1.5	1	2	4.5	2

b)

c) 23 hives

Q5 a)

No. of hours	Frequency	Frequency density
$0 \leq h < 1$	6	6
$1 \leq h < 3$	13	6.5
$3 \leq h < 5$	15	7.5
$5 \leq h < 8$	9	3
$8 \leq h < 10$	23	11.5
$10 \leq h < 15$	25	5
$15 \leq h < 20$	12	2.4

b) 103 students
c) $8 \leq h < 10$ (i.e. the class with the highest frequency density)

d)

e) 41 students

Q6 a)

Milk (litres)	Frequency	Frequency density	Mid-interval	Frequency × mid-interval
$0 \leq C < 1$	6	6	0.5	3
$1 \leq C < 5$	6	1.5	3	18
$5 \leq C < 8$	6	2	6.5	39
$8 \leq C < 10$	6	3	9	54
$10 \leq C < 15$	6	1.2	12.5	75
$15 \leq C < 20$	6	1.2	17.5	105

b) 20 litres
c) 8.2 litres (to 1 d.p.)
d)

e) 16 days

Answers

Q7 a)

Salary S, (£1000s)	$0 < S \leq 10$	$10 < S \leq 20$	$20 < S \leq 30$	$30 < S \leq 40$	$40 < S \leq 50$
Frequency	10	25	42	20	3
Frequency Density	1	2.5	4.2	2	0.3

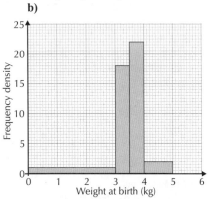

b) E.g. there are more people with higher salaries now than 10 years ago.

Q8 a) He has plotted the frequency, not the frequency density.

b)

Q9 You need to use the frequency densities shown on the histogram to calculate the frequencies, as in this table.

Class	Frequency density	Frequency	Mid-interval value (x)	fx
0-20	7	140	10	1400
20-25	28	140	22.5	3150
25-30	45	225	27.5	6187.5
30-35	37	185	32.5	6012.5
35-40	18	90	37.5	3375
40-60	11	220	50	11 000
		1000		31 125

So an estimate of the mean test score is
31 125 ÷ 1000 = 31.1 (to 1 d.p.)

Pages 130-131 — Other Graphs and Charts

Q1 $\dfrac{360°}{100} = 3.6°$ per gram

Carbohydrate	$3.6 \times 35 = 126°$
Protein	$3.6 \times 15 = 54°$
Fat	$3.6 \times 10 = 36°$
Magical Fairy Dust	$3.6 \times 40 = \underline{144°}$
	$360°$

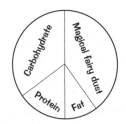

Q2 Sherrington 380 000 = 146° (approx)
2600 visitors ≈ 1°
So, to the nearest 10 000:
Brompton = 2600 × 119° ≈ 310 000
Barny = 2600 × 44° ≈ 110 000
Livsea = 2600 × 51° ≈ 130 000

Q3 a) Monday, Wednesday and Thursday
b) Monday
c) 14

Q4 It's not possible to tell whether more people voted for the Green Party in 2010, because you can't tell how many people voted in either election.

Q5 a) About 60%
b) About 10%

Q6 a) See the graph below.
b) 4
c) The 4-point moving averages you need to plot are: 20.75, 21.25, 21.75, 22.25, 24.5, 25.25, 25.5, 26, 25.75, 25.75, 26.5, 27.25, 25.75
The trend is shown by the straight line on the graph. It is clearly rising as time passes, showing that the amount spent on sun cream rises as the years pass.

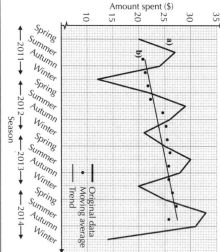

Q7 Complaints have stopped rising, so that part of the statement is true. But there are still about 10 850 per month, every month — this suggests the products aren't being made to a higher quality. The second part of the statement doesn't seem to accurately describe the data.

Page 132 — Scatter Graphs

Q1 a)

b) The variables show a strong positive correlation.
c) The greater the height, the bigger the shoe size.
d) 9

Q2 a), b)

c) Candidate 5
d) Approximately 45%

Q3 a), b)

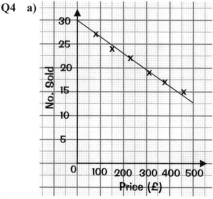

c) There is a weak positive correlation between the price of a cookery book and the number of pages it contains.
d) An accurate reading from your line of best fit, e.g. £8.
e) A book with 450 pages doesn't fall inside the range of the data, so the line of best fit may not be valid for this many pages.

Q4 a)

b) i) 20 (to nearest whole number)
ii) £140 (± £10)
c) The data shows a strong negative correlation.

MHW46B_MXHW46B